WEED CONTROL
IN
FARM AND GARDEN

AGRICULTURAL AND HORTICULTURAL STUDENTS SERIES

GENERAL EDITOR

J. HUNTER SMITH, M.B.E., M.C., B.SC., N.D.A., N.D.D.

PRINCIPAL 1921–1950 'OAKLANDS', ST. ALBANS

HERTFORDSHIRE INSTITUTE OF AGRICULTURE AND HORTICULTURE

AGRICULTURAL AND HORTICULTURAL
STUDENTS SERIES

WEED CONTROL
IN FARM
AND GARDEN

STEPHEN J. WILLIS
B.Sc.(Agric.)

ASSISTANT LECTURER IN AGRICULTURAL SCIENCE
'OAKLANDS', ST. ALBANS

HERTFORDSHIRE INSTITUTE OF AGRICULTURE
AND HORTICULTURE

With 20 Illustrations
and 16 figures in text

VINTON & COMPANY LIMITED
Stratford Place, London, W.1

First published in 1954

*Printed in Great Britain
by The Anchor Press, Ltd.,
Tiptree, Essex*

As a small token of my
love and thanks I
DEDICATE
this book to my
MOTHER AND FATHER

CONTENTS

NOTE

Throughout this book the common names of weeds and
crop plants are used. With a few exceptions the Latin names of
weeds and some crop plants only accompany the common
names on the first occasion when they are used. For the sake
of easy reference the common names are listed in alphabetical
order, together with their Latin equivalents, in the Glossary
at the end of the book. Some alternative common names of
British weeds are also given there in a separate list, followed
by the English meanings of Latin words often used in plant
names.

LIST OF ILLUSTRATIONS

LIST OF TABLES

PREFACE

FARM Institute students only make up a very small section of either the farming or the scholastic communities and it is, perhaps, for this reason that so few books are available, suited to their special needs. It is in an endeavour to satisfy such a need, in at least one subject, that this book on weed control has been written.

My aim has been twofold, firstly, to combine practical recommendations with sufficient theory to enable students to approach weed problems intelligently, rather than by rule of thumb, and secondly, to set down the whole in such a way that a person with little scientific knowledge and a limited experience of agriculture or horticulture can understand it.

While the Farm Institute audience has been my primary concern, I hope at the same time that the subject matter will also be of interest and value to practising farmers and growers, and even the soil-conscious public in general.

S. J. WILLIS

St. Albans,
 1954.

CHAPTER ONE

WHY CONTROL WEEDS?

THE main purpose in this book is to discuss the methods used in the control of weeds, but, before doing so, it seems only logical to ask why we should bother to control weeds at all. Many answers have been given to the question, but for the moment we want to concentrate on the fact that WEEDS DETRACT FROM THE VALUE OF LAND. Indeed it is probably true to say that a plant only becomes a weed when it does detract from the value of land. The standard of "value" will, of course, vary with the use to which the land is put. Thus with a flower garden, rockery, or even a cemetery, the standard of value will be an aesthetic one and any plant which, in the opinion of the observer, spoils their beauty will constitute a weed. With a playing field, a lawn, a bowling green or a park, the standard of value will be one of utility and any plant which, in the opinion of the player, reduces its playableness or, in the opinion of the user, its usefulness, will be termed a weed. In the case of a commercial holding, such as a market garden or a farm, the standard of value will be one of financial profit and any plant, therefore, which reduces the financial profit should, in the eyes of the cultivator, be deemed a weed.

You will notice that in the last sentence we use the word "should" instead of "will". We do this intentionally, for while the aesthete will be quite sure that a particular plant is spoiling the beauty of the flower-bed, or the sportsman that a particular plant is interfering with his play, or the pleasure-seeker that sitting on a thistle in the park hinders his enjoyment, the commercial grower is often reluctant to admit (and sometimes rightly so) that a particular plant is causing him a loss of profit, especially if the plant itself is going to be costly to eradicate. Leaving then the first two types of depreciation to speak for themselves, let us take a look at the ways in which "weeds" can cause losses to the commercial grower. The first

and most important of these is that WEEDS CAUSE REDUC-
TIONS IN CROP YIELDS.

COMPETITION

Like other living things plants have certain essential needs
for growth, namely water, light, carbon dioxide, oxygen,
warmth and various nutrients obtained from the soil. If a crop
is denied its full requirement of one or more of these essentials,
because it has to share them with weeds, its growth will suffer
and its yield will be reduced. We say that the weed is in
COMPETITION with the crop. The most important forms
of competition between crop and weeds are those for nitrogen
(one of the nutrients obtained as salts from the soil), light and
water.

Salts containing nitrogen are required in large quantities
by most plants (except Legumes), besides which they are
easily washed out of the soil by water. Thus, under conditions
of cultivation, nitrogen salts in the soil are frequently in short
supply and if a crop has to compete with weeds for nitrogen it
will almost certainly suffer and its yield will be lowered. A
good example of this is seen in some results from a sugar beet
experiment carried out at the Woburn Experimental Station.
In the experiment some of the plots were weeded and some
left unweeded. Half the weeded and half the unweeded plots
received a dressing of a nitrogen fertilizer while the remainder
received no nitrogen. The results are given in Table 1.

TABLE 1

Effect of weeds and nitrogen on the yield of Sugar Beet at Woburn*

WASHED BEET. TONS PER ACRE

Sulphate of Ammonia cwt./acre	Crops kept		Reduction in yield due to weeds
	Weeded	Unweeded	
0	11·68	9·45	2·23
4	15·47	15·43	0·04

* *Soil Conditions and Plant Growth*. Sir E. John Russell; revd. E. Walter
Russell. (Longmans, Green & Co.)

You will see that where no nitrogen was applied the weeds caused a considerable reduction in yield, but where more nitrogen was available it eliminated the competition of the weeds. Just as with nitrogen, so weeds can also compete with crops for the other soil nutrients, particularly potash and phosphate, but the nitrogen effect is usually considered the most important.

TABLE 2*

Effects of irrigation on growth of sugar beet over a period of three years

YIELDS OF SUGAR. CWT. PER ACRE

Year	Centre	Rainfall over growth period	0·4† cwt. nitrogen per acre		0·8 cwt. nitrogen per acre	
			Irrigated	Not irrigated	Irrigated	Not irrigated
		ins.				
1948	Milford	10·7	—	—	68	67
1949	Milford	5·0	44‡	36	44½‡	35
1949	Kesgrave	5·2	54	30	50	31
1950	Kesgrave	10·5	63‡	52	61½‡	55

* "Experiments on the irrigation of sugar beet". H. L. Penman. *J. Agric. Sc.* (1952), 42; 3; 286–92.
† 0·4 cwt. nitrogen = 2 cwt. sulphate of ammonia (approx.).
‡ Average of two sets of treatments.

Competition for light is also important, but only takes place when one plant is large enough to shade another. Thus, whereas in the case of competition for nitrogen both crop and weed suffer if it is short, in the case of competition for light, only one or the other suffers, i.e. the one in the shade. This is important because, while large weeds may shade a crop and cause serious loss of yield, if the crop can be encouraged so that the position is reversed then the weeds may be eliminated. The control of weeds by the use of "SMOTHER CROPS" is based on this principle.

Competition for water must also not be overlooked. The growth of plants is dependent on their ability to carry out the process called TRANSPIRATION, and that, in turn, is dependent upon an adequate supply of water to the plant's roots. For much of the year rainfall is more than adequate to supply the plant's needs, but during the summer months, when rainfall is usually lowest and the plant's need greatest, there is often a deficiency. In fact formulae have been worked out whereby it is possible to calculate from meteorological data when such deficiencies, due to the amount of transpiration exceeding the amount of water available, are likely to occur. Using these formulae as a guide, experiments on the use of irrigation in sugar beet have shown that considerable increases in yield can be obtained by correcting the water deficiency. (*See* Table 2). If the yields of crops are reduced through an inadequate water supply during the Summer months, how much more will this be the case if they have to share that water with a crop of weeds!

Before leaving the subject of competition it is worth noting that with certain associations of crops and weeds, e.g. barley and certain weed grasses, reductions in yield have been demonstrated even when all the necessities for growth are in adequate supply. It must be emphasized, however, that there is also evidence that this does not apply to all associations of weeds and crops; on the contrary, it is possible that in a few such associations weeds exercise no competitive effect at all (e.g. poppies in Spring cereals).

The reduction of yields due to competition is undoubtedly the major factor contributing to the financial loss caused by weeds, but we shall now consider some other factors which also must not be overlooked.

WASTAGE

1. *Weeds cause waste.*—To elaborate we shall take examples of three types of waste; perhaps you can think of others. Firstly, weeds waste time. The obvious point here is that where weeds are present in crops, time will have to be spent on extra cultivations and special operations to eradicate them, but weeds also waste time in more subtle ways. For example,

sheaves of corn which are full of thistles will not be handled so quickly as clean ones; seed which is harvested with weed-seed impurities will cause more time to be spent in cleaning it; large quantities of weeds in potato crops will hinder the lifting machinery; weed seedlings hiding crop rows will slow down inter-row cultivations, and so on.

Secondly, weeds waste space. Weeds in pasture, for example, are occupying space which might otherwise be filled with useful grasses providing food for stock. Furthermore, where weeds are present in pasture, cattle will often try to avoid them, leaving large patches of grass untouched, so increasing the waste. A good example of this was provided by an experiment* on the control of Bulbous Buttercup (*Ranunculus bulbosus*) in pasture by the use of the so-called "hormone" weedkillers (*see* Table 3).

TABLE 3

Weight of herbage ungrazed in an experiment on the control of bulbous buttercup in pasture

DRY MATTER, CWT. PER ACRE

	Buttercups controlled with		*Buttercups not controlled*
	M.C.P.A.	*2, 4–D*	
Weight of ungrazed herbage	8·2	9·2	15·6
Extra herbage grazed	7·4	6·4	Average 6·9

It will be seen that where the Buttercups were killed by the weedkillers much more grass was grazed than where they were left uncontrolled. In the rest of the field the same thing happened, giving the appearance of numerous islands of grass and Buttercups amidst a sea of well-grazed herbage.

Here too we must include the overgrown hedge, for even

* *Agriculture* (1950), 57; 8; 359–64. S. J. Willis.

hedges become weeds when they exceed a size necessary to fulfil their useful functions of enclosure and shelter.

Thirdly, weeds waste manures and fertilizers. Just as one does not "throw pearls to feed swine", so it is equally true that one cannot afford to waste manures and fertilizers on weeds, and yet this is exactly what does happen, at least in part, when they are applied to weedy crops.

HARM TO STOCK

2. *Weeds may cause harm to stock.*—A large number of wild plants are to some degree poisonous to stock and not a few of these cause death if eaten in any quantity. A list of some common wild plants which can cause death in animals is given in Table 4.

TABLE 4

Poisonous wild plants which may cause death in animals

Pasture Weeds	*Arable Weeds*	
Bracken	Black Mustard	
Celery-leaved Crowfoot	Corn Buttercup	
Common Hemlock	Corn Cockle	
Common Henbane	Poppy	
Darnel	White Mustard	
Foxglove		
Greater Celandine	*Hedge Climbers*	
Meadow Saffron	Black Bryony	
Ragwort	Deadly Nightshade	
Tansy	Woody Nightshade	
Water Dropwort		
Water Hemlock	*Trees and Shrubs*	
Water Parsnip	Box	Laburnum
	Broom	Privet
	Elder	Yew

Despite this rather imposing list one must not get the idea that domestic animals are dying every day from eating poisonous plants; on the contrary, deaths caused by these plants are amazingly few, simply because animals rarely eat them. The times when accidents are most likely to occur are when herbage is so plentiful that it is difficult for stock to separate weeds from grass, or during periods of drought when grass is dried up and a juicy weed becomes an attractive morsel. Only a few of the weeds retain their poisonous properties when made into hay, but those that do may also cause trouble in this respect. Other cases of poisoning have been traced to animals browsing hedges or to their eating hedge cuttings which have been dumped on pastures by someone too lazy to burn them!

Other weeds which, although not poisonous, may cause trouble with stock are (a) the Horsetails (*Equisetum spp.*), due to their hindering milk secretion when eaten; (b) weeds like Wild Onion (*Allium vineale*), Onion Couch (*Arrhenatherum tuberosum*), Chamomiles (*Anthemis spp.*), Yarrow (*Achillea millifolium*), which can cause taints in milk, and (c) thorn-bearing weeds which may cause inflammation of the tongue, producing a condition not unlike "Wooden Tongue" (*Actinomycosis*).

PARASITISM

3. *Weeds may be parasites.*—In one sense all weeds may be parasites, but in the strict sense a weed is only a parasite when it derives its livelihood directly from another plant. Although truly parasitic weeds are not common, a few are of some importance, particularly the Dodders (*Cascuta spp.*), the Broomrapes (*Orobanche spp.*) and Yellow Rattle (*Rhinanthus minor*). These weeds derive their food from another plant, called the "Host", by means of suckers, and as this process often results in the death of the host (which may be an important crop plant, e.g. clover), their presence can be very serious (for control, *see* Chapter Fifteen).

ALTERNATIVE HOSTS

4. *Weeds help to perpetuate diseases and pests.*—Every commercial grower will be aware of the damage done to his crops by pests and diseases. Despite all the measures taken to control them they still appear year after year. The reason for this is partly that in spite of efforts made to control them in crops, the pests and diseases are able to survive on other plants; such plants we call "Alternative Hosts". Many of our common weeds can act as alternative hosts and a list

of some of these, together with the pests and diseases they help to perpetuate, is given in Table 5.

TABLE 5

Some Weeds which can act as alternative hosts

DISEASE OR PEST	*ALTERNATIVE HOSTS*
FUNGUS DISEASES:	
Club Root (Finger and Toe) (*Plasmodiophora brassicae*)	Many weed members of the family "Cruciferae", e.g. Charlock, Shepherd's Purse, Runch, etc.
Take-all (Whiteheads) ... (*Ophiobolus graminis*)	Bents (*Agrostis spp.*), Yorkshire Fog and possibly other grasses.
VIRUS DISEASES:	
Cucumber Mosaic	Many different weeds including both Monocotyledons and Dicotyledons.
Tomato Spotted Wilt ...	Bindweed, Plantain, and many other weeds.
APHIS VECTORS OF VIRUS DISEASES:	
Peach Aphis ... ... (*Myzus persicae*)	Charlock, Shepherd's Purse, Black Nightshade, Stinging Nettle and many other weeds.
Cabbage Aphis ... ... (*Brevicoryne brassicae*)	All weed members of the family "Cruciferae".
INSECT PESTS:	
Flea Beetles ... ... (*Phyllotreta Spp.*)	Charlock, Shepherd's Purse, Runch and other Cruciferous weeds.
Frit Fly (*Oscinella frit*) ...	Some weed grasses.
EELWORMS:	
Tulip Root of Oats ... (*Anguillulina dipsaci*)	Chickweed, Field Mouse-ear Chickweed, Cleavers, Sandwort and others.
Sugar Beet Root Eelworm ... (*Heterodera schactii*)	Fat Hen, Charlock, Shepherd's Purse, Runch, Treacle Mustard, Hedge Mustard, Chickweed, Docks, Knotgrass.
Chrysanthemum Eelworm ... (*Aphelenchoides ritzema-bosi*)	Ox-eye Daisy, Groundsel.

It is doubtful, whether, in some cases, this action of weeds is very important, as even were the weeds all controlled there are still ample alternative hosts in the hedgerows and amongst other crop plants. In a few cases however it is certain that by controlling weeds we are doing a great deal towards controlling the pests and diseases to which they act as hosts. For example, the disease of wheat and barley called "Take-all" can be controlled by means of a two-year break in the rotation from those two crops, but if during the two years the ground is infested with the alternative hosts of Take-all, then the rotational control will be of none effect. The same is also true of the eelworm pest of oats causing the condition called "Tulip Root", except that in this case the break from Oats *and the alternative hosts* must be considerably longer.

We trust that enough has been said about the ill effects of weeds to convince you they are thoroughly bad and that it is well worth while studying how to prevent and control them.

CHAPTER TWO

WEED PREVENTION

THE old saying that "*prevention is better than cure*" is just as true of weeds as it is of most other maladies, but the ways in which it can be applied are few. This, however, only makes it all the more urgent that we practise those few means of prevention which are open to us.

Hard though it is to believe, weeds do not appear by magic, but grow from seeds or vegetative parts (e.g. pieces of rhizome or tap root, bulbs, bulbils, corms) which are either already in the ground or are brought there by some physical agency. Let us examine these two possibilities in more detail.

SEEDS OR VEGETATIVE PARTS ALREADY IN THE GROUND

Many weed seeds and some vegetative organs exhibit a phenomenon called "DORMANCY"; that is they remain alive in the ground but do not germinate or grow. Such dormancy may be of one or two types, either NATURAL or INDUCED. Natural dormancy lasts, usually, only for a few months, although in some cases (e.g. Wild Oat) it may persist for several years, and is part of the natural life cycle of the plant. In other words it is the normal behaviour for each generation of seed of that species of plant to have a period of rest before it germinates. Induced dormancy, on the other hand, is an abnormal phenomenon resorted to by seeds and vegetative parts which find themselves in situations quite unsuitable to their growth. Charlock (*Sinapis arvensis*), for example, is a plant which likes arable conditions and so if a Charlock seed finds itself buried in a firmly consolidated pasture it does not germinate but becomes dormant. If the pasture is ploughed up and the Charlock seed is still alive, then it will germinate and grow, a fact which explains many peculiar Charlock appearances during the period of the war-time plough-up policy. The rhizomes of Creeping Thistle (*Cirsium arvense*) also exhibit induced dormancy and react in a very similar way to Charlock seeds. Some of the periods for which weed seeds can remain alive in the soil without germinating are given in Table 6.

TABLE 6

Periods for which it is possible for various weed seeds to remain viable in the soil*

Up to 3 years	Up to 10 years	Up to 20 years	Up to 30 years	Up to 40 years or more
Couch (*Agropyron repens*) Wild Oats (*Avena fatua*)	Chickweed (*Stellaria media*) Shepherd's Purse† (*Capsella bursa-pastoris*) Pennycress (*Thlaspi arvense*) Ribwort (*Plantago lanceolata*)	Curled Dock† (*Rumex crispus*) Charlock (*Sinapis arvensis*) Broad-leaved Plantain (*Plantago major*) Creeping Thistle (*Cirsium arvense*)	Pesicaria (*Polygonum persicaria*) Ox-eye Daisy (*Chrysanthemum leucanthemum*)	Broad Leaf Dock (*Rumex obtusifolius*) Fat Hen (*Chenopodium album*) Black Nightshade (*Solanum nigrum*)

* Abstracted from *J. Agric. Res.*, 72; 6; 201–10. E. H. Toole and E. Brown (1946).
† Will live longer when buried deeply.

SEEDS WHICH ARE INTRODUCED INTO THE GROUND

Those seeds and vegetative parts of weeds which are not already in the ground are brought on to our farms and gardens by various physical agencies. These agencies can be grouped under five main headings:

(*a*) Wind and water.
(*b*) Birds and animals.

(c) Dirt on implements.
(d) Dung and compost.
(e) Seed impurities.

(a) A number of seeds, such as those of Dandelion (*Taraxacum officinale*), Thistles, Hawkbits (*Leontodon spp.*) and Maple (*Acer campestre*), are provided with special attachments to enable them to be carried by the wind, and even seeds which are not so equipped may be blown about if they are sufficiently light. Many seeds are also carried in streams and rivers, but it is doubtful if these are of direct practical importance except perhaps in the case of meadows and fields which are periodically flooded.

(b) Birds are often unconscious disseminators of seeds because many of the seeds they eat pass through them without being harmed and are ejected in their droppings. To a lesser extent this is also true of animals, the seeds of Fat Hen (*Chenopodium album*) and Chickweed (*Stellaria media*) being two notable examples, but animals also disseminate seeds through carrying them about on their fur or fleeces. Here again, a number of plants, such as Cleavers (*Galium aparine*), Corn Buttercup (*Ranunculus arvensis*) and Knapweed (*Centaurea nigra*), have seeds or fruits specially equipped with spines which catch on to the coats of animals brushing against them.

(c) That seeds may be carried from place to place in the soil adhering to tools and implements I suppose is obvious, but the numbers carried in this way are possibly larger than we imagine. Academically speaking, this is easily avoidable, but on a farm scale cleaning implements before they pass from one field to another is not always either practical or economical. Nevertheless tools and machines which are regularly cleaned and oiled last longest, and certainly there is no reason why many of the smaller tools and implements should not receive this treatment at the end of each day's work.

(d) The normal biological activities going on inside dung and compost heaps should destroy most weed seeds within three weeks, but it is known that some seeds will survive for considerably longer periods. A tentative list of these is given in Table 7.

TABLE 7

Weed seeds that may remain alive in dung and compost

For periods longer than 3 weeks	For very long periods (i.e. several months)
Hoary Pepperwort (*Cardaria draba*)	Lesser Bindweed (*Convolvulus arvensis*)
Docks (*Rumex spp.*)	Fat Hen (*Chenopodium album*)
Dodders (*Cuscuta spp.*)	
Chickweed (*Stellaria media*)	

When dung or compost containing such seeds is applied to the soil, the seeds have, of course, ideal conditions for growth, thus getting away to a very quick start and proving a greater menace than might otherwise be the case.

(*e*) Finally, it is an unpleasant fact that growers may actually be sowing weed seeds as impurities in their crop seeds. In fact the "sowing of Wild Oats" is probably more literally true than we like to realize!

Having seen why weeds appear in our crops, we can now formulate one or two ways of preventing them. Firstly we have seen that the large bulk of our weed troubles begin as weed seeds, and when it is realized what colossal numbers of seeds some of our common weeds produce, it is not surprising that weeds are a major problem. Table 8 gives the numbers of seeds produced by some of our common weeds and, if anything, the figures given are on the low side. In the words of another old adage, "One year's seeding is seven years weeding."

TABLE 8

Numbers of seeds produced by some common weeds*

Weed	No. of Seeds per Plant
Charlock ... ... (*Sinapis arvensis*)	1,000
Dandelion ... ... (*Taraxacum officinale*)	3,000
Fat Hen ... ... (*Chenopodium album*)	3,000
Scentless Mayweed ... ... (*Matricaria maritima*)	34,000
Sowthistle ... ... (*Sonchus oleraceus*)	8,000

* From *Kampen mod Ugraesset*. E. Korsmo (1906). (Figures given to nearest thousand.)

Obviously, then, our first preventive measure must be to stop weeds running to seed wherever possible. The situations where seeding is most likely to occur are lawns, pastures, hedgerows and waste places. Seeding should not have a chance to occur in cultivated land, as here weeds are best controlled while they are still seedlings, at which stage they have done least damage to the crop and are easiest to kill. In lawns seeding can be prevented by regular mowing. In pastures, which are not being kept for hay, a mower, set high, should be used periodically to cut off the flowering heads of weeds while they are still in the bud. In hedgerows and waste spaces every endeavour should be made to prevent seeding either by cutting back or spraying. Here again, as in pastures, the best time is when the weed is in the flower-bud stage, as then the plants are usually most vulnerable, thus giving a better chance of control.

Occasionally the source of weed seeds is one we cannot touch, namely our neighbours' ground! Unfortunately, there is little we can do to enforce people to kill weeds except in the case of five particular species. Under *The Injurious Weeds Order* *of* 1921 the appropriate authority* can enforce the destruction of weeds listed as "Injurious". The weeds (*see* Figs. 1 and 2) at present listed are:

Ragwort (*Senecio jacobea*) Spear Thistle (*Cirsium vulgare*) Creeping Thistle (*Cirsium arvense*) Curled Dock (*Rumex crispus*) Broad-leaved Dock (*Rumex obtusifolius*)

Figure 1.   Ragwort
By permission of H. C. Long

Secondly we should endeavour to see that the seeds we use are free of weed-seed impurities. When buying seed, we are in the hands of our merchant, but provided he has a good reputation and a name to uphold, then usually we need have little to fear about the purity of his seed. When using your own seed, see it is taken from a clean crop and is given as thorough a riddling as your equipment will allow. Where there is any doubt about the purity of seed a small sample (about a pound), *taken at random*, can be sent to the appropriate Seed Testing Station for the area (*see* Appendix I) for a "purity test".

In this question of seed purity we are again helped by the Law. *The Seeds Act of* 1920 and the *Seeds Regulations of* 1922,

* County Agricultural Executive Committees in the case of agricultural land, County Councils in other cases.

Spear Thistle
(*Cirsium vulgare*)

Creeping Thistle
(*Cirsium arvense*)

Curled Dock
(*Rumex crispus*)

Broad-leaved Dock
(*Rumex obtusifolius*)

Figure 2.   Some Injurious Weeds
By permission of L. Reeve & Co. Ltd.

which apply to any vendor of seeds whether he be farmer, grower or merchant, require certain specified seeds, when sold or offered for sale, to be accompanied by a declaration, of their percentage purity.* If "injurious weed seeds" (i.e. seeds of Docks, Sorrels (*Rumex spp.*), Cranesbills (*Geranium spp.*), Wild Carrot (*Daucus carota*), Yorkshire Fog (*Holcus lanatus*) and Soft Brome (*Bromus mollis*) are present to the extent of more than 5% by weight of the sample, then it is illegal to sell or offer the seed for sale as seed. The seeds specified under the Regulations include:

Grass and Clover Seeds
  Perennial Ryegrass
  Italian Ryegrass
  Meadow Fescue
  Cocksfoot
  Crested Dogstail
  Timothy
  Red Clover
  Alsike Clover
  White Clover
  Crimson Clover
  Trefoil
  Lucerne
  Sainfoin

Cereal Seeds
  Wheat
  Barley
  Oats
  Rye

Garden Seeds
  Peas
  Dwarf and Broad Beans
  Runner Beans
  Garden Turnip
  Garden Cabbage
  Garden Kale
  Garden Kohl Rabi
  Garden Swede
  Brussels Sprouts
  Broccoli
  Cauliflower
  Carrot
  Parsnip
  Beet
  Onion

  Flax Seed and Linseed
  Also Forest Tree Seeds of
    various types

Field Seeds

  Tares or Vetches
  Field Turnip
  Swede
  Rape
  Field Cabbage
  Sugar Beet

  Field Kale
  Field Kohl Rabi
  Mangel
  Field Peas
  Field Beans

* Except in the case of cereals. In the case of Field Seeds and Garden Seeds the percentage purity has to be stated only if it is below 97% or, in the case of carrot seed, below 90%.

Some other requirements concerned with weed seeds are:

1. The total percentage of injurious weed seeds must be declared in writing, if present to the extent of more than 1% in clover seeds or 2% cent in grass seeds;

2. If Dodder is present to the extent of more than one seed in

    1 oz. Wild White Clover;

    2 oz. White Clover, Alsike Clover, Timothy;

    4 oz. Red Clover, Crimson Clover, Lucerne, Flax, Linseed,

a statement must be made to that effect.

3. In Sainfoin seed it must be stated if more than 5% by weight of Burnet (*Poterium spp.*) is present.

The Seeds (Amendment) Regulations of 1942 provide for the sale and sowing in England, under licence granted by the Ministry of Agriculture, of seed mixtures containing more than 5% of Yorkshire Fog. The licences, however, are only granted for the use of approved mixtures on land specified in the licence.

Thirdly, certain precautions should be observed in the making of compost and dung heaps. Compost heaps are the most likely to give trouble and in making them one or two simple rules should be observed:

1. Do not make compost heaps too small. To ensure that weeds seeds are killed, the compost heap must be able to "heat up", but this does not happen to a sufficient extent in small heaps.

2. Provide optimum conditions for bacterial activity. If the materials are mature (i.e. low in nitrogen), a source of nitrogen should be added to the heap as it is built up. This may be made in the form of sulphate of ammonia, nitro-chalk, or cyanamide. If sulphate of ammonia is used chalk or limestone should also be added as the heap is built up to neutralize the acidity produced by the rotting process. Alternatively to this procedure a proprietary compost-making preparation can be used.

3. Over-compactness is a frequent fault in compost making; good aeration is essential for heating up.

4. Avoid putting seed heads on the compost heap, particularly those of the plants in Table 7.

5. Do not put plants of Bindweed (*Convolvulus arvensis*), Creeping Thistle and Docks on the compost heap; burn them instead.

As far as dung is concerned the main points to be noted are:

1. Do not put loft sweepings on the dung heap.

2. Avoid using litter that may contain weed seeds, particularly those of Chickweed and Fat Hen.

Apart from the desirability of cleaning tools and implements, previously noted, there is little else one can add on the question of prevention in weed control.

CHAPTER THREE

WEED CONTROL BY GOOD PRACTICE

LATER on in this book several chapters will be devoted to a discussion on the control of weeds by chemicals; this being inevitable because of the rapid advances made during the last decade in the development of such chemicals and the ever increasing use being made of them by farmers and gardeners. It is, however, none the less true that chemicals can never take the place of GOOD HUSBANDRY, and that where this is practised the need to use chemicals will be at a minimum. This does not mean that the rules of good husbandry have been drawn up for the sole purpose of controlling weeds, but it is true that weed control has been a very potent factor in influencing the evolution of many of the best cultural methods in use today.

It is not one of the objects of this book to deal at length with the methods of good husbandry as they affect every aspect of farming and gardening, but in this chapter we hope to outline a few of the more important practices which have some bearing on the control of weeds.

GOOD PRACTICE IN ARABLE CROPPING

In the growing of arable crops, whether it be in farm or garden, growers' practices are very diverse and, often, equally good, but even here it is possible to lay down a few general rules of cultivation which help in the control of weeds.

1. *A good rotation.*—Just as with crops, the conditions for growth enjoyed by one group of weeds may be quite unsuitable for another group. As a result, different groups of weeds tend to become associated with particular crops. In corn crops, for example, we tend to find weeds like Poppy (*Papava rhoeas*), Charlock, Corn Gromwell (*Lithospermum arvense*), Corn Buttercup, Scarlet Pimpernel (*Anagallis arvensis*) and Parsley Piert (*Aphanes arvensis*); in root and potato crops weeds such as Fat Hen, Persicaria (*Polygonum persicaria*)

and the Nightshades (*Solanum spp.*), while in market gardens we find Speedwells (*Veronica spp.*), Groundsel (*Senecio vulgaris*), Chickweed and Annual Nettle (*Urtica urens*). Under the conditions of a good rotation, where a succession of different crops is being grown, favourable conditions for any one set of weeds are never in vogue long enough for them to become established. The differences between the floras of grassland and arable are too obvious to require listing, so it is not surprising that where land is alternating between these two, as in ley farming, the effect on weeds is considerable. Even the alternation of Autumn and Spring crops, so that cultivations are done at different times, has a considerable effect in controlling some weeds, e.g. Black Grass. Of course, one always gets the "couldn't-care-less" type of weeds, such as Thistles and Docks, which seem to grow anywhere, but we can class these as "the exceptions which prove the rule".

Another way in which rotations help in weed control is in the regular occurrence of so-called "CLEANING CROPS". Do not be misled by this term; it is the grower, not the crop, who does most of the cleaning! A cleaning crop is one which allows a good deal of cultivating, and hence weed-killing, to be done while the crop is growing and which subsequently gives a good cover to the ground, thus smothering out (*see* Chapter One) any weeds which may be left. Examples of cleaning crops are potatoes, mangolds, sugar beet and cabbages.

2. *Thorough cultivations.*—The main object of cultivations is to prepare land for sowing or planting, and the success of the crop is often very dependent on how well these cultivations are done. Cultivations also have a direct action in controlling weeds, either, as in the case of ploughing, by burying them or, as in disking, cultivating, harrowing, raking, etc., by injuring young seedlings. In both cases, however, the extent of the weed control achieved will depend on the thoroughness with which the cultivations are carried out.

3. *Liming.*—There are few arable crops in Britain which do not benefit from a non-acid soil and for many this is essential for successful growth. Some weeds, on the other hand, of which Spurrey (*Spergula arvensis*), Knawel (*Scleranthus annuus*) and

Sheep's Sorrel (*Rumex acetosella*) are the main offenders, seem to thrive in acid soils. Added to this the poor growth of crops in acid soils gives the weeds plenty of room to spread. Thus, by correcting acidity, with the use of lime or chalk, we are exercising a direct control on some weeds and an indirect effect on many others.

4. *The full use of land.*—Such is the abundance of weed seeds in the fertile British soil that no ground will remain bare for long. Far better that it should be covered with something profitable than with something unprofitable or even deleterious. While not forgetting that, with the commercial grower, economics always come first, it seems only common sense to make the fullest use of our land, not only by bringing into cultivation waste corners and going as near to the edges of fields as is possible, but also by the use, where practicable, of such methods as catch cropping and inter-cropping.

Finally, all practices which enable crops to grow quickly and strongly help indirectly in weed control, in that they place the plants in a strong position to compete against and overcome the invading weeds.

GOOD GRASSLAND MANAGEMENT

The weeds of pastures and grassland can be divided into two main groups: firstly, there are the more obvious types such as Buttercups, Daisies (*Bellis perennis*), Dandelions, Thistles and Ragwort; secondly, there are the less obvious weed grasses such as Yorkshire Fog, Creeping Soft Grass (*Holcus mollis*), Bents and Bromes. A sward made up of these grasses is little better than one containing a profusion of the other weeds. Weed control in grassland must, therefore, aim at eliminating both types. Fortunately the best pasture grasses such as Perennial Ryegrass (*Lolium perenne*), Cocksfoot (*Dactylis glomerata*), Timothy (*Phleum pratense*) and the Meadow Grasses (*Poa spp.*) are well able to stand up for themselves against all types of weeds provided they are given good conditions for growth. At the same time, however, we must not forget those equally important constituents of good pasture, the clovers, for, unless we are careful, the useful grasses will oust these along with the poor grasses and weeds.

The task of grassland management is, therefore, twofold: it must aim at producing a strong and vigorous sward of the best species of grass and, at the same time, maintain a proper balance between the grasses and clovers. Where this task is properly performed the weed problem will be of minor importance.

A few of the more important practices in good grassland management are as follows:

1. *Drainage.*—Clovers and useful grasses cannot survive in a wet soil, and where such a condition exists their place will quickly be taken by water-loving weeds, such as Rushes (*Juncus spp.*), Sedges (*Carex spp.*), Crowfoots (*Ranunculus spp.*) and Buttercups and other poor herbage. Adequate drainage, therefore, is the first essential for a good pasture.

2. *Liming.*—As was stated earlier in this chapter, there are very few crops in this country which prefer an acid soil, and for many crops the correction of acidity by liming or chalking is essential to good growth. This is very true in the case of clovers and pasture grasses. It also happens that a number of those plants which seem to thrive under acid conditions are just the plants we do not want in pastures, namely Creeping Soft Grass, Yorkshire Fog and Sheep's Sorrel.

From both points of view, encouraging the good and discouraging the bad plants—liming—or, better still, chalking—is an essential part of grassland management on soils which have even a tendency to acidity. Where pastures are very acid a dressing of "small chalk" (unprocessed chalk from fine dust to lumps about the size of a cricket ball) applied in the Autumn at a rate of 10 tons per acre, is a good remedy, which should not need repeating for 10 to 15 years. Alternatively a dressing of ground chalk or limestone, at the rate of 2–3 tons per acre applied in the Autumn and repeated every eight or ten years, can be used. Where the soil has only a tendency to acidity a dressing of 20–25 cwt. per acre of ground chalk applied about every five years should maintain the pasture in good condition.

3. *Alternate mowing and grazing.*—Shutting up a pasture for hay has the effect of increasing the grasses at the expense of the clovers, whereas close grazing benefits the clover at the

expense of the grass. A wise alternation of grazing and mowing for hay, therefore, enables a proper balance of grass and clover to be maintained as well as ensuring that the fullest use is made of the pasture. A suitable programme might be something like the following:

1st Year

(*a*) Stock have access during January and February.
(*b*) Shut up the field in March and take an early hay-cut.
(*c*) Graze the aftermath during the summer.
(*d*) Shut up the field from early Autumn until the following March.

2nd Year

(*e*) Graze the early bite in the Spring.
(*f*) Rest to allow the grass to recover.
(*g*) Take a late hay crop.
(*h*) Rest until October to allow the grass to recover.
(*i*) Graze during the Autumn.
(*j*) Shut up the field in December until the following Spring.

3rd Year

(*k*) Graze the early bite in the Spring.
(*l*) Rest and graze alternately for the rest of the year.

4th Year—as 1st Year

4. *Correct Manuring.*—Nitrogen fertilizers benefit the grasses at the expense of the clover, while phosphatic fertilizers do just the reverse, and so, here again, a wise combination of the two is required. Nitrogen should be applied each year, during February, particularly when an early bite is required.

Nitro-chalk, at 2–4 cwt. per acre, is best used where there is a tendency to acidity or sulphate of ammonia, at 1½–3 cwt. per acre on chalky soils. Phosphates are probably best applied as basic slag, or ground mineral phosphate, particularly on acid soils, but superphosphate can also be used and may be advantageous on very chalky soils. The particular period in the management programme when phosphatic fertilizers are applied is not of much importance and applications of moderate dressings can be repeated about every three years after a rather heavier initial dressing. Basic slag can be applied during the Winter at the rate of 3–5 cwt. per acre of a medium grade or superphosphate in the Winter or early Spring at a similar rate.

Potassic fertilizers should be regarded as of equal importance to phosphatic ones and used at similar rates if 20% potash salts are available, otherwise use an equivalent amount of muriate of potash.

Other practices which help in maintaining a vigorous, and therefore weed-free, sward are mixed grazing with cows and sheep and harrowing the pastures during Winter and after periods of intensive grazing.

The preceding discussion applies only to pastures which already have a good proportion of useful grasses and clovers. Where pastures have been neglected so that they have become poor and weedy, by far the best approach, wherever practicable, is to plough them up and start again. The land can either be reseeded direct with a suitable seeds mixture or, better still, it can be put through an arable rotation and then sown down under a cover crop. When direct reseeding grassland in the Spring, it is a good tip to include a bushel of oats in with the seeds mixture. Grazing of the sward can then begin earlier than would otherwise be the case and a number of benefits result. Not least of these is a better control of weeds—a very important factor in obtaining a good establishment of grass.

GOOD LAWN MANAGEMENT

The requirements of a good lawn are nearly the exact opposite to those of a good pasture. Clover, for example, may

be the idol of the farmer but it is the bane of the grounds-
man; while, on the other hand, grasses such as Sheep's
Fescues (*Festuca spp.*), which are weeds of pastures, are the
"pride and joy" of the lawn. It is to be expected then that
good lawn management will diverge considerably from good
grassland management. The aim of lawn management is to
produce a dense, closely knit turf of hard-wearing, fine-
leaved grasses, and where this can be done there will obviously
be no room for weeds.

One of the most important operations in lawn management is mowing. The rule here is to mow regularly, often, and
not too hard. If the interval between mowing is too long the
grasses tend to assume a tall open habit of growth which
allows space for weeds and causes the mowing to have a much
greater damaging effect on the grass. Infrequent mowing also
allows weeds to produce seed and so multiply. Mowing
which is too "close", particularly if only carried out infre-
quently, weakens the grasses so that they are unable to
compete successfully with weeds, particularly the rosette
types.

Another major difference between lawns and pastures is
that lawns grow better on a moderately acid soil. The acidity
has two main effects: firstly it favours the fine-leaved grasses
rather than the coarse ones and, secondly, it discourages some
weeds, particularly some clover species. Acidity in lawns can
be maintained and encouraged by the use of sulphate of
ammonia or lawn sands. Lawns do occasionally become too
acid (pH below 4·8–5·0) so that even the fine-leaved grasses die.
This condition can be identified by the fact that the turf has a
spongy feeling underfoot due to a thick layer of old, unrotted
leaves covering the ground. Also, when the turf is raked it
comes away in chunks leaving bare patches of soil. Where
extreme acidity occurs a light dressing of ground chalk should
be applied to the grass at the rate of $\frac{1}{4}$–$\frac{1}{2}$ lb. per square yard,
depending on whether the soil is light or heavy.

Two further important functions of sulphate of ammonia,
and lawn sands, are the provision of nitrogen, the plant food
most needed by lawn grasses, and, particularly in the case of
lawn sands, the direct control of weeds. Sulphate of ammonia

(or an equivalent of lawn sand) should be applied at the rate of ½ oz. per square yard in the Spring. Lawn sands are mixtures of sulphate of ammonia, calcined sulphate of iron and sand. The usual proportions are

3 parts sulphate of ammonia,
1 part calcined sulphate of iron,
20 parts sand,

although a more drastic weed action can be achieved with a mixture using half this quantity of sand. Lawn sands should be applied two or three times during the growing season at fortnightly intervals using 4 oz. per square yard. The weeds which can be satisfactorily controlled by lawn sands include:

Wild White Clover (*Trifolium repens var sylvestre*)
Daisy
Mouse-ear Chickweed (*Cerastium vulgatum*)
Ribwort (*Plantago lanceolata*)
Selfheal (*Prunella vulgaris*)
Sheep's Sorrel
Birdsfoot Trefoil (*Lotus corniculatus*)
Yellow Suckling Clover (*Trifolium dubium*)

Finally the elimination of earthworms is also quite an important factor in controlling weeds in lawns. Under normal conditions of cultivation worms are highly beneficial but in lawns they are a nuisance because of their casts. Not only may the wormcast contain dormant seeds brought up from the sub-soil but it forms a projection on which weed seeds can lodge and a patch of bare soil in which they can germinate. The casts can be broken up by brushing or raking but if they are not to reappear the worms must be eliminated. One method of doing this employs a material called "Mowrah meal". The meal is applied as a fine, dry powder, at the rate of 6–8 oz. per square yard, and then watered in with plenty of water (at least one gallon per square yard). The worms will come to the surface and die and should then be swept up. The treatment usually needs to be repeated about every two years.

WEED CONTROL IN ORCHARDS

It is now accepted as good practice to grass down orchards once the trees are well established. Where this is done the grass should be kept short by mowing, particularly during the fruit-blossom time, and the combined effects of the grass and the mower will keep most weeds under control. While orchards are getting established, or where it is considered unwise to grass down an orchard (e.g. in a frost pocket), the weeds should be kept down by ploughing between the trees during the Winter and by occasional cultivations during the Summer. Ploughing should not be taken too near the trees for fear of disturbing the roots.

CHAPTER FOUR

SPECIAL METHODS OF CULTURAL CONTROL

By ADOPTING sound methods in farm and garden practice, the need for special weed-control measures will be reduced to a minimum, but even in the best-run holding special methods will have to be adopted on occasions. In this chapter we shall discuss the main cultural practices adopted in farms and gardens for the particular purpose of controlling weeds.

HAND WEEDING

In spite of all the modern machines and chemicals, there are still situations where the only way to deal effectively with weeds is to pull them up by hand. Such is the case, for example, wherever weeds are inaccessible by machines, and chemicals cannot be used because of the resistance of the weeds or the susceptibility of the crop plants, e.g. flower-beds, herbaceous borders, shrubberies, etc. There are three important rules to observe when hand weeding. Firstly, pull up as much as possible of the weed, including roots and other underground parts. Many weeds, such as Docks and Bindweed, are able to regenerate if a portion, and particularly the crown, of their root is left in the ground. Other plants like Thistles, Couch (*Agropyron repens*) and Stinging Nettles (*Urtica dioica*) have underground stems (rhizomes) which if left behind in the soil will also produce new plants. Parts of the plant which are above the ground and which are capable of producing new plants are also sometimes left behind; for example, a number of weeds produce stems (runners or stolons) which trail over the surface of the ground and which root at their nodes to produce new plants. Often the runners are very brittle, so that when the main bulk of the weed has been pulled up a few small rooted nodes are left behind which in a few weeks will have produced a new crop of weeds. Plants of this type to beware of are Cinquefoil (*Potentilla reptans*), Wild White

Clover, Creeping Buttercup (*Ranunculus repens*), Chickweed and Creeping Soft Grass. Another plant, Onion Couch, produces a string of corms at the base of its stem which are often left behind when the plant is pulled up. These too are able to produce new plants.

Secondly, having pulled up the weed, it should be removed and destroyed. Unless the weather is very dry, weeds which are left on the surface of the ground will quickly produce new roots and suffer no more than a slight setback. Suitable weeds should be put on the compost heap, but where there is any doubt of their seeds being destroyed by composting (*see* Chapter Two) they should be burned.

Thirdly, do your hand weeding before the weeds produce their flowering heads. By doing this, you are not only destroying one weed but thousands of potential weeds as well.

A number of tools have been invented for assisting in the work of hand weeding. The tool called a spudder (*see* Fig. 3A)

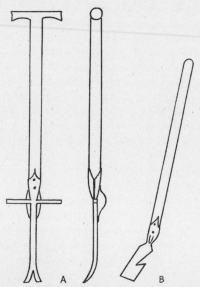

Figure 3. A.—Spudder, front and side
elevation. B.—Thistle Hoe

is very useful for removing weeds with a strong root system. To operate it, the prongs of the instrument are pushed under the plant, which is then levered up by pressing down the handle on to the pivot just behind the prongs. Another tool to help in hand weeding is the "thistle hoe" (*see* Fig. 3B), which consists of nothing more than a V-shaped cutting notch mounted on a stick so that thistles can be cut off near the ground. The other tools for hand weeding are all included in the general term "hoe", but hoeing is such a wide subject that we shall now devote a special section to it.

HOEING

In the past hoeing has been performed for a number of reasons, but it is now fairly certain that much of the benefit derived from it is in the control of weeds.

Sir William Ogg, the Director of Rothamsted Experimental Station, has said:* "A great deal of hoeing and inter-row cultivation is done in the belief that the loose surface layer checks the evaporation of water from the soil. It has been shown, however, that this is not the case and that the benefits obtained are largely due to the destruction of weeds which compete with the crop. Even seedling weeds take up a great deal of both water and plant food and have a markedly depressing effect on crop growth in the early stages, a check from which crops seldom fully recover. Hoeing and other surface cultivations are, therefore, of great value in killing weeds, but they are apt to damage the roots of crops and should be restricted to the minimum necessary for weed control."

Recent American work, however, suggests that this may be a somewhat extreme point of view. Experiments at the Connecticut Agricultural Experimental Station† have shown that *under some conditions of soil and weather* inter-row cultivations do give some benefit apart from weed control. This is attributed to the beneficial effect of aeration on the soil micro-population. The work is also particularly interesting

* *Jour. Royal Soc. of Arts* (1951), *100*; 4870; 371–2. Sir William Ogg.
  † *World Crops* (1951), 3; 9; 345–8. C. L. W. Swanson and H. C. M. Jacobson.

in that chemical weedkillers are used to provide control conditions in an experiment on the physical structure of the soil.

Although methods of hoeing are almost as numerous as are the types of hoe, the aim behind the operation is the same for them all. It is to sever the top of the plant from its root by cutting it just below the soil surface. Essentially, then, a hoe is a cutting blade so arranged that it can be made to move through the soil at the required depth.

Hoes can be divided into two main groups: hand operated and machine operated. The various types of hand hoes are as follows:

Figure 4.   Some types of Hoe blades.   A.—Draw hoe.
B.—Swan-necked hoe.   C.—Dutch hoe.

(a) *Draw Hoe* (Fig. 4A).—A draw hoe consists of a flat blade about 4 in. or 5 in. wide and mounted on a long handle in such a way that the angle of the blade, with the handle, is less than 90° and the edge of the blade is towards the operator. The arrangement should be such that when the hoe blade is lying flat on the ground, the handle can be held by the operator comfortably in both hands while he is in the standing position. In actual practice it is usually necessary to adopt a slightly stooping posture to use the ordinary draw hoe and, as this is very tiring, many workers prefer the "swan-necked" hoe (Fig. 4B), which requires less back-bending. The cutting action of the draw hoe is achieved by the operator "drawing" the blade towards him through the soil. In addition to controlling weeds, the draw hoe is also used for ridging potatoes and for singling.

(b) *Dutch Hoe* (Fig. 4C).—A Dutch hoe consists of a flat

rectangular blade mounted at an obtuse angle to a long handle in such a way that the edge of the blade points away from the operator. Its cutting action is achieved by pushing it through the soil, and for this purpose the Dutch hoe requires fairly loose soil. It is particularly useful for hoeing in amongst bushy and overhanging plants, which would interfere with the action of a draw hoe.

(c) *Onion Hoe* (Fig. 5).—The onion hoe is like the swan-necked version of the draw hoe, but with a smaller blade and only a very short handle. It is operated like a draw hoe, but from a kneeling position, so that small crop plants can be more easily seen and avoided.

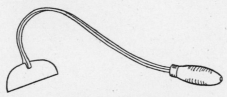

Figure 5.   Onion Hoe

(d) *Wire Hoes*.—These hoes employ a fine wire, stretched between two prongs, as a cutting agent instead of a blade. One type has four prongs supporting a square of wire, the hoeing being carried out by moving it forwards and backwards or from side to side. To be effective, wire hoes must be used in a very fine tilth.

(e) *Wheel Hoes* (Fig. 6).—These consist of a single wheel, the axle of which is supported between the ends of two long curved handles. Mounted just behind the wheel on a bar fixed between the handles is either a single hoe blade about 8 in. wide or a number of small V-shaped blades. These machines are used for hoeing between rows of plants which are set fairly wide apart. The operator pushes the tool in front of him using a reciprocating (i.e. backwards and forwards) action.

Machine-mounted hoes are all more or less the same in principle (Plate 1b). They consist of a tool bar, either mounted on wheels or attached directly to a tractor, to which can be bolted different designs of hoe blades according to the type of work required. The wheel models can be drawn by either tractors or horses. The hoe blades, which are carried so that they lie parallel to the ground, are usually of two types, L-shaped and V-shaped. The blades are arranged on the tool bar so that as much as possible of the ground is hoed without actually touching the rows of the crop.

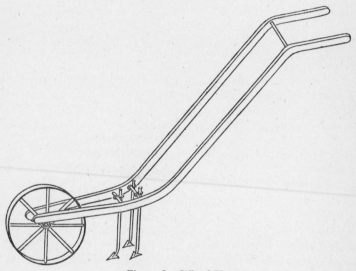

Figure 6.   Wheel Hoe

Hoes of this type require only one man to operate them, but if they are to get very close to the crop plants the rows must be very straight. To overcome this objection the "steerage hoe" was devised. In this type the tool bar is so arranged that it can be steered between the rows of plants by a second operator sitting at the rear. One very ingenious steerage hoe also has a device which can actually work between the plants in the row. This consists of two blades which can be opened to go round the crop plants by means of a foot pedal.

With some crops which are slow in germinating, hoeing cannot be carried out as early as is desirable, because the crop rows cannot be seen. To overcome this difficulty a MARKER CROP can be used. This consists of a few seeds of a quick-germinating crop, such as radish or lettuce, mixed in with the slow-germinating seeds, to give an early indication of the position of the crop rows and enable hoeing to proceed.

Another type of machine-driven hoe which can be very effectively used for killing weeds is the rotary hoe. In this the hoe blades rotate from an axle and are whirled round by a motor to give the hoeing action. The machine is used for all sorts of purposes besides weed control and can be adjusted to work at various depths. When set to work at a shallow depth it can be very useful for weeding between rows of plants such as raspberry canes and fruit bushes.

So much for hoes, but two final points about hoeing. Firstly, the action of severing a plant from its roots is most likely to be successful if the plant to be killed is young. The hoeing of weeds, therefore, is most effective when carried out while the plants are as young as possible, preferably while they are still in the seedling stage. Apart from this it is much less hard work than having to hack at matured plants.

Secondly, for a hoe blade to cut, it must be reasonably sharp. Of course it is not necessary that you should be able to shave with it, but many hoes would do better work for seeing a grindstone occasionally! In this connection it is interesting that a hoe has been designed which uses old hack-saw blades, so that the blade can be replaced when it wears out or breaks.

FALLOWING

Fallowing is probably one of the oldest weed-control practices in this country and was even a feature of the manorial system in Norman England. Like hoeing, although several forms of fallowing are employed, the basic principle is the same for all of them. The purpose of a fallow is to kill weeds by persistently damaging them or causing them to be dried up in the soil and by encouraging weed seeds to germinate. There are two types of fallow practised in this country: the bare fallow and the bastard fallow.

(a) *The Bare Fallow.*—The true bare fallow is usually employed under heavy land conditions. Its aim is to get the land into large clods, about the size of a football, which can be periodically turned during the Summer months, so that they become thoroughly dried. The drying of the clods kills the weeds they contain, while the continual movement gradually breaks them down so that by the end of the Summer there is a very fine tilth. This tilth causes any weed seeds that are left alive to germinate, and the plants they produce are destroyed by the ploughing in preparation for the Autumn crop. The typical procedure for a bare fallow is as follows:

1. Leave the land uncultivated until April to give as many weeds as possible the chance to grow.

2. Plough the land deeply in April and then, 10 days to a fortnight later, either cross-plough or cultivate to produce a very cloddy condition. This operation should not be begun before April as the Winter frosts would then break down the clods and the object of the fallow would be lost.

3. Whenever an opportunity arises during the following months move the clods about with a plough or cultivator, so that they become thoroughly dried. The plough is the better implement as there is less breakage of the clods.

4. By about the beginning of August the clods will have been broken down into a tilth and the field should be rested to allow any weed seeds present to germinate.

5. Plough in the weeds during September or October ready for the Autumn crop.

In lighter-land districts a different form of bare fallow is sometimes practised. In this the land is ploughed and cross-ploughed at intervals beginning in the Autumn and carrying on to the following Summer. In this case the weed-killing effect is probably due more to the continual movement of the land than to the drying out of the furrow slices.

Apart from the weed-killing value, bare fallows do have other useful effects, such as conserving moisture and increasing the availability of plant nutrients in the soil, but they also have certain disadvantages. Firstly, and most important of all,

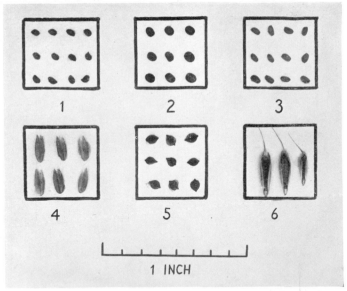

Photograph by H. W. Gardner

1a. Some injurious weed seeds: 1. Dove's-foot Crane's-Bill (*Geranium Molle*). 2. Cut-leaved Crane's-Bill (*Geranium dissectum*). 3. Small-flowered Crane's-Bill (*Geranium pusillum*). 4. Yorkshire Fog (*Holcus lanatus*). 5. Curled Dock (*Rumex crispus*). 6. Soft Brome (*Bromus mollis*)

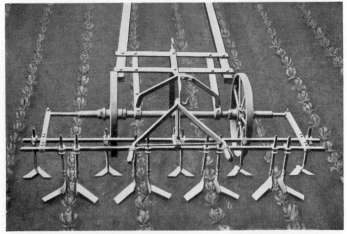

Photograph by F. Randell

1b. A horse-drawn steerage hoe

Photographs by Imperial Chemical Industries Ltd.

2a and 2b. A sward before and after treatment with fortnightly applications of sulphate of ammonia between May and September at a rate of 1 lb. per 200 sq. ft. and watered in

the fallow land brings no financial return to the farmer for a whole year; in fact, allowing for time and labour spent in cultivation, it is a loss. Of course it can be argued that the weed control and other advantages achieved will bring in an increased return in the years following the fallow, but then weeds can be controlled by other methods which do not involve any loss of cropping. Whether or not a bare fallow is economically justifiable must be left to the farmer to decide, but certainly there is a case for it in heavy land which is badly infested with weeds. Secondly, there is the question of Wheat Bulb Fly (*Leptohylemia coarctata*), a pest of wheat which will only lay its eggs on bare ground. A bare fallow makes a very suitable site for the fly to lay its eggs, and as wheat usually follows a bare fallow, the chances of attack are considerable. The problem can be avoided by covering the ground with a quick-growing crop during the egg-laying period, which is in July. A suitable and commonly used crop for this purpose is mustard, which can be ploughed under in the Autumn to provide green manure. Where a crop other than wheat follows a fallow, this precaution is unnecessary. The third and last drawback to a bare fallow is that its success is dependent on a dry Summer, which is beyond the power of even the most capable farmer to arrange.

(*b*) *The Bastard or Summer Fallow.*—The bastard fallow overcomes, to a large extent, the objection to a bare fallow: that of losing one year's cropping. In principle it is exactly the same as a bare fallow except that it does not commence until June or July, thus allowing time for a quick crop. Suitable crops would be oats and tares for silage or a ley cut early for hay. Ploughing grassland early enough for a bastard fallow has the added advantage of giving the birds a chance to dispose of any wireworm which may be present. Needless to say a bastard fallow is not so effective as a good bare fallow, but it can still be very effective, provided the weather is dry.

STUBBLE CLEANING

Stubble cleaning, as its name implies, can only be practised after a straw crop. As few weed-control measures are possible in these crops after the early Spring it becomes possible for a number of weeds to grow, flower and produce seed before the crop is harvested. Thus, after harvest, there may be a large number of weed seeds scattered over the surface of the ground. Where the combine is used the position is likely to be even worse, because not only is the crop left growing longer, but also most of the rubbish is discarded back into the field with the straw. The purpose of stubble cleaning is to provide conditions which will cause as many as possible of these seeds to germinate so that they can be destroyed before the next crop is sown.

As soon as the straw crop has been harvested, or even while the stooks are still standing in the field, the surface soil is cultivated to a depth of not more than two inches and this operation is then repeated at intervals of about a fortnight. The batch of weed seedlings produced by each operation is killed by the succeeding one, while a final kill is obtained when the land is ploughed for the next crop. Although, because of the phenomenon of natural dormancy described in Chapter Two, some weed seeds will not germinate so soon after harvest, stubble cleaning is a very effective way of controlling a number of important weeds, e.g. Charlock, Chickweed, Groundsel, Runch (*Raphanus raphinistrum*), Shepherd's Purse (*Capsella bursa-pastoris*) and Speedwell. It is to be regretted that it is not more widely adopted. Indeed there is a lot to be said for making it a regular feature of the farm routine.

Suitable implements for carrying out stubble cleaning are the broadshare, a cultivator with broadshare tines, or a thistle bar. Where none of these are available a very shallow ploughing can be employed, or even a light disking.

AUTUMN CLEANING

Many of the weeds which, because of their dormancy, are unaffected by stubble cleaning can be killed by what we shall call, for want of a better term, Autumn cleaning. The principle in Autumn cleaning is to play a trick on those weeds which germinate in the Autumn and early Spring and which, there-fore, flourish in Autumn-sown crops. The trick is to prepare a seed bed in the Autumn as though in readiness for a crop and then not to sow anything until the Spring.

One writer* has said that some clay-land farmers of his acquaintance "would go so far as to advocate running the drill over the land, without, of course, filling it with seed, on the assumption that black grass never grows until it hears the rattle of the drill coulters!" This is, perhaps, going a bit too far, but it conveys the right idea. Following the preparation of the seed bed, the weed seeds concerned germinate and the seedlings produced can be subsequently killed by cultivating at intervals of about a fortnight, as the weather permits. A final kill is obtained by a ploughing after Christmas in preparation for the Spring crop, or, alternatively, in very weedy fields stirring of the soil can continue at intervals until the following summer. The latter practice, however, amounts to another form of bare fallow.

Weeds which can be controlled by Autumn cleaning include: Black Grass (*Alopecurus agrestis*), Charlock, Corn Buttercup, and Shepherd's Needle (*Scandix pecten-veneris*). The method has the disadvantage that the highly beneficial action of frost may be lost.

THE SCARLETT METHOD

An ingenious method of cultural control of weeds in badly infested land has been developed by Mr. Robert Scarlett†; it combines the good effects of cultivation and green manuring with the fertilizing and weed-killing properties of calcium cyanamide.

The land is ploughed during the Winter or early Spring and sown with tares (vetches) at the rate of $1\frac{1}{2}$ cwt. per acre in February or early March. When the tares produce their first flowers, towards the end of June, they are crushed with a heavy implement and calcium cyanamide is applied at the rate of 3–4 cwt. per acre, preferably while the dew is on the plants. Six to eight days later the ground is again ploughed, making sure that all the green material is covered. A rough seed bed is then prepared and during the early weeks of July rye is sown at a rate of two bushels per acre. The growth of rye is ploughed under during the Winter, followed by a second

* *Agriculture* (1940), 47; 1; 42. W. S. Mansfield.
† *Scot. Jour. of Agric.* (1937), 20; 1; 41–5. Robert L. Scarlett.

ploughing in preparation for a Spring crop, such as potatoes, sugar beet, cabbage, turnips, mangolds or silage.

Like the bare fallow, this method is subject to the criticism that a whole year's cropping is lost, but it has two advantages over the bare fallow: (1) less work is involved and (2) it is not subject to weather conditions. Mr. Scarlett defends it on the grounds that where land is very weedy many successive crops are often lost. The method also has the advantage that by replacing ploughing with digging it can be practised on a garden scale.

I am assured this method does work very well and it would seem, therefore, that it could be put to good use under certain circumstances.

FLAME GUNS

Although not strictly a method of cultural control, this is a convenient place to discuss the use of flame-guns. These are implements, rather like a large blow-lamp, which produce a jet of flame that can be used for burning seedling weeds. They have two main uses: (1) in places where there is no vegetation, e.g. paths, drives, etc., and (2) for controlling weeds between rows of crop plants which are not injured when their outer leaves are scorched, e.g. strawberries. In the latter case the flame must not, of course, be directed on to the crop plants themselves, but only on to the growth between the plants. I am informed that to get the best use from a flame-gun large weeds should only be scorched at the first flaming, then given two days to a week (according to weather conditions) to wilt, and then be finally burnt with a second flaming. The attempt should NOT be made to destroy large weeds completely at the first flaming. Better still is to kill the weeds while they are still young. Although their usefulness is limited, flame-guns can give a good control of weeds.

CHAPTER FIVE

CHEMICAL WEED CONTROL

IT IS a well-known fact that if human beings or animals eat or drink certain chemicals, as a result they will die. The chemical which immediately springs to our minds in this connection, I suppose, is arsenic—the cause of so many murders, if not in fact, certainly in fiction! It is, perhaps, not so generally realized that many chemicals will poison plants in a similar way. Let us call them "plant poisons".

Poisoning, however, is not the means by which chemicals can kill plants. If you have ever had anything to do with the liquids called "strong acids" you will know that a drop spilt on a coat will burn a hole unless washed off quickly. Strong acids have exactly the same effect when dropped on to plants, and provided you are able to cover a large part of the plant's surface with the acid, the plant will be so badly burnt it will die.

GROWTH REGULATORS

Another, and quite different, method of killing plants can also be used. You will have noticed in growing up that various parts of your body have developed in proportion to one another. Your arms did not grow faster than your legs, nor your legs faster than your arms. This is explained by the fact that our growth is controlled by minute quantities of very complex substances, called "hormones", which are secreted into our blood streams by various glands in the body. The regular growth of plants is controlled similarly by hormones. In recent years it has been found that certain chemicals can be made in the laboratory which regulate the growth of plants very much in the same way as hormones. These chemicals are called "growth regulators". Growth regulators, however, like hormones, are only needed in very small quantities and if excessive amounts of the chemical are applied to a plant, it has the effect of distorting the plant's growth to such an extent that the plant dies. By using growth regulators in excessive amounts, then, we have another method of killing plants by chemicals.

THE PROPERTIES REQUIRED OF A WEEDKILLER

We have now described three types of chemicals which will kill plants—plant poisons, acids which burn and growth regulators. Any of these substances which will kill plants will, of course, kill those plants we call weeds, and as this is the main purpose for which we need them, we call them "chemical weedkillers" or just "weedkillers"*. Just because a chemical is capable of killing weeds it does not necessarily make it suitable for use as a weedkiller. Indeed there are a large number of chemicals which will kill weeds but the number actually used as weedkillers is quite small. It would be wise, then, at this point, to discuss what other qualifications are desirable for a chemical to possess before it can be of use as a weedkiller.

1. It should not be poisonous to either animals or man. Obviously weedkillers will often have to be used in places frequented by domestic animals and, whether these be cats or cows, we do not usually want to kill them. Perhaps more important still, a weedkiller is much less dangerous for workers to handle if it is non-poisonous. For this very reason compounds of arsenic, which were once used quite widely for weedkilling, largely fell from popularity when other substances became available.

2. It should be harmless to the soil. There are two points of importance here. Firstly, the chemical should not damage the structure of the soil. Secondly, it should not harm the bacteria, fungi and other microbes which are present in the soil and which do such important and necessary work.

3. It should be easy to handle. Here a number of points can be listed:

    A. The chemical should not be

        (*a*) explosive, highly inflammable, or give off dangerous fumes—requiring extensive precautions by workers;

* Also "Herbicides", "Weedicides".

    (*b*) corrosive—necessitating elaborate precautions being taken with machinery;

    (*c*) bulky—causing large volumes to be applied to get effective control, making application slow and transport a problem.

B. It should be in a form easy to store and apply. A deliquescent substance (i.e. one which absorbs much moisture from the atmosphere), for example, is not much use where the material is to be applied dry, or an insoluble substance when it has to be dissolved in water to make a spray.

4. It should be easy to store without losing any of its effectiveness during storage.

5. It should be cheap. If a chemical is so dear that the profit obtained from using it is exceeded by its cost, it will be difficult to persuade any farmer or grower to buy it!

Of course, no one chemical will possess all these qualities, as we shall see when we come to consider weedkillers individually, but unless it possesses a number of them, and particularly the last, it will not even be "in the running".

SELECTIVITY

All chemicals which kill plants and are eligible as weedkillers do not, however, kill all plants equally easily. Some plants need much more weedkiller to kill them than others and these we say are "resistant". It will help towards a wise use of chemical weedkillers if we understand some of the reasons for this; I say "some of the reasons" advisedly, because those that we have still do not explain all the facts. In studying the reasons for the varying effect of weedkillers on plants it will help if we consider the growth regulators separately, and for want of a better term call the remainder "contact weedkillers". The reasons we know to date, then, for the differing resistance of plants to contact weedkillers are as follows:

1. Some plants are more easily poisoned than others. An analogy with animals will probably help in understanding this point. The weed called Ragwort contains a substance which is poisonous to animals, but it is a well-known

fact that sheep can eat a lot more Ragwort than cows,
although even sheep can eat too much. Similarly with
plants; although all plants will be killed by a plant poison
provided they get enough of it, some plants need more
than others. It is, therefore, possible to apply such a
quantity of a plant poison that it will kill some plants and
not others.

2. Some plants retain the weedkillers while others do
not. If you examine the leaf arrangements of plants you
will find that, by and large, they fall into one of two types:
those with leaves which are narrow and have a tendency
to grow at right angles to the ground (i.e. Monocotyledons),
and those with leaves which are broad and have a tendency
to grow parallel to the ground (i.e. Dicotyledons). When a
weedkiller, whether dry or in solution, is put on to a plant
of the latter type the leaves tend to hold the weedkiller and
the plant is killed, whereas in the former type the weedkiller tends to roll off the leaves and the plant receives
little damage. Here again the amount of weedkiller is
important; even the plants with narrow, upstanding leaves
will be killed if too much is applied, but with suitable
quantities of weedkiller the one type of plant will be killed
and the other receive little hurt. When one remembers
that so many of our farm crop plants, e.g. wheat, barley,
oats, rye, are of the Monocotyledonous type and many of
our most important weeds are of the Dicotyledonous type,
it will be realized how important this point is.

3. Some plants have their growing points protected.
To kill a plant successfully the growing point must be
killed or the plant may survive. In some types of plant
such as wheat, barley, oats and grasses, the growing point
is protected by sheathing leaves. With these plants the
weedkiller is usually unable to penetrate to the growing
point and so, although the leaves are killed, the plant is
able to recuperate.

4. The leaves of some plants are protected by waxy
coatings. You will have noticed that if you drop water on a
waxy or greasy surface it forms itself into small spherical
drops. The same thing happens if a weedkiller is sprayed

(i.e. applied as a solution) on to plants with waxy leaves; the spray forms into drops and rolls off. It is for this reason substances called "Wetting Agents" (*see* page 66) are sometimes added to sprays, as they counteract the effect of the leaf-surface. The waxy coating on the leaves also protects the leaf cells from penetration, and hence damage, by the weedkiller. Thus plants with waxy leaves tend to escape the effects of contact weedkillers.

Summing up these four reasons, one can make the general statement that the CONTACT WEEDKILLERS are more effective against the Dicotyledonous type of plant than the Monocotyledonous type.

As far as the GROWTH REGULATORS are concerned it is difficult to give a reason for their varying effect on different plants; one can only make the rather obvious statement of fact that some plants are able to tolerate a greater amount of the chemical than others. It is possible that the second reason given for contact weedkillers may also be applicable here, but the resistance of Monocotyledons to growth regulators is not so well defined as it is in the case of contact weedkillers.

From the last few paragraphs it will be seen that at *specified rates* (i.e. a stated quantity of chemical per a stated area, e.g. 20 lb. per acre, 1 pint per square yard) a chemical weedkiller, if applied to a mixed group of plants, will tend to kill some and not others. Such a chemical we say is SELECTIVE. If one or more of the plants it does not kill are crops and some of those which it does kill are weeds we have a SELECTIVE WEEDKILLER. Thus we may define a selective weedkiller as a chemical which at *certain specified rates* of application will kill *certain specified weeds* and *leave certain specified crops* unharmed. I have emphasized parts of the definition because it is important to realize that no selective weedkiller has yet been discovered which will kill *all* weeds and not affect *any* crops. Quite the reverse is the case, as each of the selective weedkillers we know at present can only be used safely in a few crops and will kill only a limited range of weeds.

E

CLASSIFICATION OF WEEDKILLERS

Summing up this chapter, then, we can group chemical weedkillers as follows:

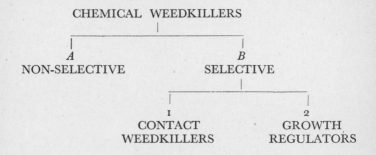

The term "non-selective" is a bad one and it is only used in this book for the sake of convenience and for the want of something better. None of the weedkillers in this group described in Chapter Eight are entirely non-selective.

In fact it is true to say that almost any weedkiller can be put into either category A or B depending on the amount applied. In practice, however, many chemical weedkillers are not sufficiently selective to make them of much use in category B, while the selective weedkillers are either not sufficiently efficient or too dear to compete with those already classified in category A. Thus, despite the failings of the nomenclature employed, the weedkillers in the two categories can be considered as fairly distinct.

The subdivision of the selective weedkillers is quite distinct, depending on the mode of action of the various substances. It is also of some practical importance because, arising out of their differing mode of action, the two types have differing properties. These can be summed up as follows:

1. Because the contact groups kill only where they touch, they leave roots and rhizomes (underground stems) unharmed. This does not matter very much with annual plants, but with perennial plants it means they can often regenerate and form a new plant. Because growth regu-

lators are carried throughout the plant internally, killing all parts of it, they can deal with perennial weeds better than the contact group.

2. The contact weedkillers act fairly quickly, in a matter of a few hours, whereas the growth regulators may take a fortnight or more to completely kill a plant.

3. As plants get older they tend to be able to withstand the effect of contact weedkillers better than when they are young. The growth regulators, on the other hand, are often more effective against older plants.

So much then for what is meant by chemical weedkillers and how they are classified. In the next chapter we shall explain some other terms associated with the practice of chemical weed control.

CHAPTER SIX

SOME TERMS EXPLAINED

LIKE all other branches of human activity chemical weed control has developed its own jargon, but this can only be of value if its meaning is understood. Before proceeding further let us be quite sure we understand the meanings of the technical terms used in the chapters to follow.

SPRAYS AND DUSTS

The *Oxford Dictionary* defines a spray as "liquid flying in fine drops", but, as the term is applied to chemical weed-killers, a better definition would be "a liquid which is capable of flying in fine drops", or, more simply, "a weedkiller in the form of a liquid, a solution or a suspension". It follows that a spray may be one of four things; it may be:

(a) A liquid chemical which is applied undiluted, e.g. light oil.

(b) A liquid chemical which is diluted before application, e.g. sulphuric acid.

(c) A solid chemical, e.g. copper chloride or the salts of growth regulators, which is dissolved in water or some other inert liquid, i.e. one which has no deleterious effect on plants.

(d) An insoluble solid, e.g. dinitro ortho cresol, or liquid dispersed throughout another liquid in the form of fine particles or drops (i.e. a suspension).

These points are not so academic as they may at first seem, as it is important, when purchasing spray materials, to realize exactly what is being bought. Particularly is this true in the case of materials in category (c), as some of these, e.g. copper sulphate, are sold as the pure solid material and others, e.g. the salts of growth regulators, as concentrated solutions which have to be further diluted. As, in this book, the rates of application of weedkillers are all given in terms of the pure material, where preparations are sold as concentrated solutions it is important to know the proportion of pure chemical they contain.

The case of dusts is similar to that of sprays but much less complicated. A weedkiller is described as "a dust" when it is used in the form of a finely divided powder. The powder may be one of two things: it may either be the pure chemical in a finely divided state, e.g. sodium chlorate, or it may be the pure chemical, e.g. salt of a growth regulator, diluted by mixing with another inert powder called a "filler", e.g. chalk, fuller's earth. Where a weedkiller can be applied as a dust and where, because of the small quantity required, it has to be diluted it is usually sold with the filler already incorporated. Here again it is important to know the proportion of pure weedkilling material contained in the bought product.

High- and Low-volume Spraying

There are two factors to be noted when diluting a weed-killer for the purposes of application:

(*a*) The strength or quantity of weedkiller required to fulfil the function for which it is intended.

(*b*) The quantity of material necessary to make even application a practical possibility with the machinery available.

In the case of spraying, most of the machines used before about 1948 could not apply evenly less than 80–100 gallons of liquid per acre. As this was also a convenient dilution at which to use any of the known weedkillers it was adopted as a standard. Such a high rate of dilution, however, required the use of large quantities of water and because this often had to be carried over long distances, when none was available in the vicinity of the field being treated, spraying was not so popular as it might otherwise have been. The introduction of the weed-killers of the growth-regulator type rather altered this situation. As these were used in such very small quantities it seemed unnecessary to use such large volumes of water, and accordingly simple spraying machines were devised which could apply volumes of between 5 and 40 gallons per acre. The new machines were called "Low-volume" sprayers and by inference the older type became "High-volume" sprayers. Of course, it was only a matter of time before someone brought out the "all-purpose" sprayer which could work at both low- and high-volume rates.

The low-volume sprayer, besides its low water consumption, has another big advantage over its rivals in that, owing to its simple construction, it is relatively cheap, being only about a quarter the cost of its all-purpose relative.

The low-volume sprayer, however, is not the whole answer to the water problem, because there is still the question of either the strength or quantity of the weedkiller to be applied. As a result, although in many cases it is safe to use the growth regulators at low-volume rates, this is not the case with the other weedkillers, and for these a high-volume machine is still necessary. Nevertheless the low-volume sprayer has been a big advance in weedkilling practice, so much so that, for many farmers, spraying has now changed from a vanity to a routine.

WETTING AGENTS

Wetting agents are chemicals which when mixed with sprays enable them to adhere more firmly to the leaves of plants. They are also called "spreaders" or "surface-active agents". Largely their action is to reduce the surface tension of the spray solution, so that when it falls on to a waxy or greasy leaf it spreads out over the surface instead of forming into droplets and rolling off.

There are many different types of wetting agents, but for the present purpose they can be divided into three groups:

1. Soft soaps.
2. Sulphonated oils.
3. Other types.

Soft soaps are usually added to the spray solution at the rate of 1 lb. per 10 gallons and sulphonated oils at 1 lb. per 100 gallons, while the other types are used at rates varying between

¼ lb. and 1 lb. per 100 gallons, but in all cases users should be guided by the manufacturers' instructions. On no account must those of the soft-soap type be used with sulphuric acid.

Spot Treatment

Spot treatment is the term applied to the application of weedkillers to individual weeds. It may be used for one of two reasons: either because the weedkiller in question, e.g. sodium chlorate, would damage surrounding plants if applied generally, or because the weeds to be controlled are too few and too widely separated to make general application of the weedkiller to the area economically desirable.

Pre-emergence Application

Pre-emergence application is the term employed when weedkillers are applied to a crop after it has been sown or planted, but before it emerges through the soil surface. It is only possible where crop seeds, such as those of onion, are slow in germinating, so that the seed bed becomes covered with a mat of weed seedlings before the crop appears. To be able to kill the weeds at this stage is often a considerable advantage, but it cannot be done by cultural operations because of the difficulty of identifying the crop rows with any accuracy. In these circumstances it is very convenient if a chemical weedkiller can be used. A similar situation also arises in beds of flower bulbs before the shoots emerge.

Not all weedkillers are suitable for pre-emergence work, as it is essential that they be very quickly inactivated on reaching the ground. Weedkillers which remain active in the soil would kill the crop as it emerged from the seeds. The most suitable weedkiller for this purpose is sulphuric acid and in many cases this is the only one that can be used.

Acids, Salts and Acid Equivalent

Acid equivalent is a term which is used only in connection with weedkillers of the growth-regulator type. In explaining its meaning we can also profitably explain the meaning of the terms "acid" and "salt".

The term "acid" is used to describe a very large group of

chemicals of which some are solids, some liquids and some gases; some very unpleasant substances which burn, and some so pleasant that they are used in making sweets.

All acids, however, have one thing in common, in that they can be considered to consist of two parts or RADICLES: one called the ACID RADICLE and the other, for which we will invent our own name, the FIRST RADICLE. The first radicle is always made of the element hydrogen but the composition of the acid radicle varies with different acids. In sulphuric acid, for example, the acid used in batteries and accumulators, the acid radicle is composed of sulphur and oxygen and is given the name "SULPHATE". The whole acid, therefore, is made up of hydrogen plus sulphate, and instead of sulphuric acid it would be quite correct to call it "Hydrogen sulphate".

The term "salt" describes an even larger group of chemicals than "acid". The one, however, has a very close connection with the other in that all salts could be made from the corresponding acid by replacing the hydrogen in the first radicle with another element. The salt called magnesium sulphate (Epsom salt), for example, can be formed from sulphuric acid by replacing the hydrogen with the element magnesium (the substance formerly used by photographers for making a flash). Imagine that this was done by dropping pieces of magnesium ribbon into the acid, so that the hydrogen is given off as gas and magnesium sulphate left behind. If the experiment were very carefully performed by adding magnesium to 98 oz. of sulphuric acid until no more hydrogen was evolved, it would be found that at the end 120 oz. of magnesium sulphate had been formed. In other words 120 oz. of magnesium sulphate *are equivalent to* 98 oz. sulphuric acid, or, as the chemist would say, 98 oz. is the ACID EQUIVALENT of 120 oz. of magnesium sulphate.

The acid equivalent of a quantity of salt, then, is the quantity of acid from which it could be formed.

There are, of course, many other sulphates besides magnesium sulphate, but with each the amount formed from 98 oz. of sulphuric acid would be different; here are some examples:

Potassium sulphate (i.e. sulphate of potash)   ...   174 oz.
Ammonium   ,,   (i.e. sulphate of ammonia)   ...   132 oz.
Calcium   ,,   (i.e. gypsum)   ...   ...   136 oz.

The growth regulators are also acids. In their case the acid radicle is very complex, but it is this acid radicle which is responsible for their weedkilling properties. In practice the acids themselves are very rarely used, it being more convenient to use some of their salts. Of course, the acid radicle is still present, but, as with sulphuric acid, the same weight of growth-regulator acid will produce different weights of salts.

Thus, for purposes of comparison and to avoid the necessity of making separate recommendations for each salt of a growth regulator, all the rates of application are expressed in terms of the acid equivalent.

LATIN NAMES

In conclusion this seems a convenient opportunity to raise the subject of Latin names. Many people appear to view them with suspicion, while students in particular tend to regard them as their sworn enemies. This is a pity, because Latin names have very important advantages and for the botanist they are indispensable. Three points about them are worth mentioning here:

1. Each species of plant has usually only ONE Latin name. Common names of plants vary very much from place to place, so that even in one country a single plant species may have several such names. For example, a list of alternative names for weeds mentioned in this book is given on page 162. Such duplication of names can only lead to mistakes and misunderstandings between those who work with plants, and if this even happens between workers in the same country, you can imagine how much greater confusion it causes on a world scale. These difficulties are all overcome, however, by the use of Latin names, as there is only one of these for each plant species which is accepted the world over.

2. Why Latin, you may ask. The answer is that a few

centuries ago, through the influence of Rome and later the Roman Catholic Church, Latin was used amongst educated people throughout central and western Europe. In that sense it was an international language and the description of a new species is still recorded in Latin. There is now the additional advantage that the use of Latin arouses no nationalistic prejudices.

3. Latin names are systematic. You will have noticed from the Latin names already given that they are made up of two parts. The first part signifies the group, or genus, to which the plant belongs and the second half distinguishes it from the other members of the genus. They are rather like our names, but the other way round, i.e. surname first and Christian name second. Thus immediately a botanist sees the name *Sinapis arvensis*, although he may never have heard of the plant itself he knows it belongs to the plant genus *Sinapis*, which in turn fixes its position among the families of plants.

Another valuable feature of Latin names is they have meanings which often tell us something about the plant. Thus "arvensis" tells us that a plant is found in an open field, "sylvestris" that it is found in a wood, and "officinalis" that it has been used as a medicine. The meanings of the names of some common plants are given in the Glossary, see page 164.

CHAPTER SEVEN

WEED-CONTROL ARITHMETIC

In any discussion about weedkillers a certain number of figures, concerning rates of application and the strengths of the chemicals used, are inevitable. If these figures are to be of any value we must understand not only what they mean but also how we can adapt them to suit our own particular needs. For example, most of the rates of application given in this book are in quantities "per acre", but these will not be of much use to a man with just a small garden or allotment unless he can convert them into quantities for a smaller area, say per square yard. Or again, all the quantities of actual weedkilling materials have been given in weights of the pure chemical concerned. As already mentioned, many proprietary weedkillers contain the chemical in a diluted form. Before you can use them, therefore, it is necessary to be able to calculate how much of the proprietary material is needed to give the requisite quantity of the pure chemical. The purpose of this chapter is to give some useful data and a few necessary explanations which might help to make these tasks easier.

RATES OF APPLICATION

Let us begin with rates of application. In this book the rates of application of weedkillers applied as dusts are given in either hundredweights or pounds per acre; first of all then we can calculate one or two easy relationships to convert these into rates for smaller areas.

A measure frequently used in allocating allotments is the "square rod"; there are 160 square rods to an acre. By coincidence there are also 160 stones in a ton, since 1 ton = 20 cwt. and 1 cwt. = 8 stone. We have, therefore, the very useful relationship:

TONS PER ACRE = STONES PER ROD
(The word "Square" is usually omitted before "Rod").

For example, a useful dressing of complete fertilizer for potatoes is 10 cwt. per acre, which is exactly equal to $\frac{1}{2}$ stone per rod (7 lb.).

Usually, however, for small areas we require quantities in rates per square yard. Now, a hundredweight contains 1972 ounces and an acre 4840 square yards. Thus, one hundredweight per acre equals $\frac{1972}{4840}$ oz. (i.e. 1972 ÷ 4840) per square yard. If you calculate this fraction you will find it approximately equal to $\frac{3}{8}$ and so we can say that 1 cwt. per acre equals, approximately, $\frac{3}{8}$ oz. per square yard, or in other words, 3 oz. per 8 square yards. For most practical purposes, however, it is sufficiently accurate to remember that

1 HUNDREDWEIGHT PER ACRE $\backsimeq$ 1 OUNCE PER
3 SQUARE YARDS.

Rates given in pounds per acre are not so simple to convert for small areas. Perhaps the most useful approximation is:

1 POUND PER ACRE $\backsimeq$ 1 OUNCE PER 300 SQUARE
YARDS.

In this form it is easy to convert into rates per rod, as 300 square yards is very nearly equal to 10 rods.

Rates of application of liquid weedkillers are given in gallons per acre. How to convert these to rates per square yard can be deduced from the relationship above that 1 lb. per acre $\backsimeq$ 1 oz. per 300 square yards. As there are 16 ounces in a pound and also 16 half pints in a gallon then:

1 GALLON PER ACRE $\backsimeq$ $\frac{1}{2}$ PINT PER 300 SQUARE
YARDS.

THE METRIC SYSTEM

So far we have only concerned ourselves with English units, but in foreign literature rates are given in terms of the metric system. To convert these to our system the following should suffice:

> 1 pound per acre $\backsimeq$ 1 kilogram per hectare
> 1 gallon per acre $\backsimeq$ 11 litres per hectare
> 1 litre per hectare $\backsimeq$ ¾ pint per acre

WEIGHT PER VOLUME

We can now turn to the question of the strengths of proprietary weedkillers. Although most proprietary dusts also contain the weedkilling chemicals in a diluted form, in this chapter we need only concern ourselves with the chemicals marketed in solution. Strengths of weedkillers in solution are usually given as percentages followed by the mysterious letters "w/v"; e.g. 30% w/v. This symbol means literally "weight per volume" and signifies that the percentage which precedes it is a weight expressed as a percentage of a volume, i.e. 30% w/v means 30 parts by weight per 100 parts by volume. The units used are always equivalent metric ones, e.g. grams and cubic centimetres, kilograms and litres, etc., so that if a weedkiller is said to be 30% w/v it means that 100 ccs of the weedkiller contains 30 grams of the active weedkilling chemical. To convert such an expression to English units we can use the relationship:

> 1% w/v $\backsimeq$ 1½ OUNCES PER GALLON
> i.e. 30% w/v would represent in English units nearly
> 3 lb. (i.e. 45 oz.) per gallon

We shall conclude this chapter by bringing together all these relationships into one table, but in using it remember that all but one of them, although sufficiently accurate for most practical purposes, are only approximations. For the sake of the purists exact figures have been given in brackets.

TABLE 9

Conversion Table for the Use of Weedkillers
⌒—"approximately equals".

TONS PER ACRE	=	STONES PER ROD
1 hundredweight per acre	⌒	1/3rd ounce (0·37) per square yard
1 ounce per square yard	⌒	2¾ hundredweights (2·70) per acre
1 pound per acre	⌒	1 ounce per 300 square yards (302·5)
1 gallon per acre	⌒	½ pint per 300 square yards (302·5)
300 square yards (302·5)	⌒	10 rods
1 pound per acre	⌒	1 kilogram (1·12) per hectare
1 gallon per acre	⌒	11 litres (11·22) per hectare
1 litre per hectare	⌒	¾ pint (0·71) per acre

1% w/v ⌒ 1½ ounces (1·6) per gallon

CHAPTER EIGHT

SODIUM CHLORATE AND OTHER NON-SELECTIVE WEEDKILLERS

THE term "non-selective weedkiller" describes a very varied group of chemicals which includes sodium arsenite, fuel oils, salt and certain phenolic materials. Although sodium arsenite is still marketed as a weedkiller it is unpopular and its use limited because of its dangerous poisoning properties. Fuel oils are still employed in some countries, particularly for controlling weeds on railways. Agricultural salt has to be applied fairly liberally to give a reliable result, but it can be quite useful in some circumstances : it is probably best used to keep weeds out rather than to control those already present. For this purpose it is very useful on crazy pavings and should be applied at the rate of about 4 oz. or more per square yard each year in the early Spring. Phenolic materials provide the basis of, at least, one proprietary weedkiller.

Undoubtedly the most popular non-selective weedkiller at the present time is sodium chlorate, and most of this chapter will be devoted to it, although we shall also make some mention of two others : sulphate of ammonia and C.M.U.

SODIUM CHLORATE

Sodium chlorate is a white crystalline solid which, in this country, has been used as a weedkiller since about 1920, but at the present time is rather expensive and, accordingly, is not used as much as might otherwise be the case. It is to be hoped this situation will remedy itself as the years go by. Most horticultural sundriesmen retail sodium chlorate, either as the pure chemical or a proprietary material, which can be bought in quantities as small as a pound or in drums containing half a hundredweight or more. From the point of view of use as a weedkiller the following are some of its properties.

1. It is highly inflammable or even explosive. Do not let such a startling statement put you off; it is just a warning that sodium chlorate needs to be treated with a little care. Its explosive tendency is only likely to manifest itself if the chemical becomes mixed with acids, particularly sulphuric acid. The question of inflammability is more important, particularly as the tendency is increased by contact with materials such as oil, wood, coal, clothing, sacking and dust. Provided the following rules are observed, however, there is nothing to fear:

(*a*) Store sodium chlorate well away from acid and oils and never in the same room. It is illegal to transport sodium chlorate and acid in the same vehicle.

(*b*) Store on a concrete floor where possible and certainly not on a wooden one.

(*c*) Store away from fire, heat, and inflammable materials.

(*d*) Sodium chlorate is supplied in metal containers with a lid; always store in these containers and keep the lid on when not in use. Never transfer the chemical to paper bags, sacks, or wooden bins.

(*e*) If a large area has to be treated it is worth while to wear gum boots and a rubber apron.

(*f*) If clothing becomes impregnated with chlorate, wash it in running water and dry in a warm room—NOT in front of a fire!

Perhaps a little story will serve to emphasize these precautions. A worker was once applying sodium chlorate after a heavy dew; his trousers became wet and some of the chlorate stuck to them. As the day progressed they were dried by the sun. Imagine his surprise later when, striking a match in a truly rural manner on the seat of his trousers, they suddenly burst into flames!

To minimize the fire hazard, sodium chlorate is sometimes mixed with half its weight of calcium chloride, in which case it is given the name "Atlacide". Calcium chloride is deliquescent (i.e. it absorbs water from the atmosphere) and keeps the chlorate damp. From the point of view of safety there is much to be said for using it in this form.

2. It is non-poisonous to animal life. Sodium chlorate has the very considerable advantage over its predecessor, sodium arsenite, in that it is not poisonous to animals or humans *in the quantities used for weedkilling*. When using it, therefore, there is no danger to birds, domestic animals or children. That is not to say, of course, it could not do harm to animals or humans; undoubtedly if it were consumed *in any quantity* it would have very unpleasant effects.

3. It is very poisonous to plant life. The title "non-selective" weedkiller indicates that sodium chlorate is toxic to a wide range of plants whether they are crops or weeds. That the term is a misnomer is revealed by the fact that not all plants are equally susceptible. As will be seen later, some weeds are amazingly resistant; some crops, on the other hand, are extremely susceptible. The greatest offender here is the tomato plant and particular care must be taken with this crop. For example, boxes of tomato plants should never be put down on paths which have recently (say within two months) been treated with the weedkiller, and there is a lot to be said for not using it anywhere in the near vicinity of glasshouses where tomatoes are growing. Many other crops apart from the tomato are also very susceptible and, except where used as a spot treatment, sodium chlorate must never be employed in a growing crop of any sort unless you are prepared to loose it for the sake of killing weeds. Some trees and hedges are resistant to an extent, but, until more detailed information is available, sodium chlorate should not be used in the near vicinity of even these plants.

4. It is extremely soluble in water. Sodium chlorate will dissolve in water and can, therefore, be used either as a dust or a spray. This property has, however, some undesirable effects in that the chemical may be carried in drainage water from either the ground surface or below. A case recently came to my knowledge where sodium chlorate, applied to a path running uphill, was washed down by rain on to a lawn. As a result the weeds on the path flourished, but a large area of the lawn was killed. Another case has been reported where chlorate applied to

F

a drive alongside a greenhouse was washed down into the drainage system and carried into the greenhouse, causing the death of an area of tomato plants. Obviously then the question of drainage is a factor to be borne in mind when using the weedkiller.

5. It remains in the soil. It follows from the last paragraph that sodium chlorate is washed through the soil, but this process may take some time to complete. Generally the chemical remains effective in the soil for about six months. While this figure is useful to remember some allowance must be made for soil types and rainfall. Light gravelly soils will probably clear in a shorter period of 4 to 5 months whereas a heavy clay soil will retain the chlorate for much longer periods (say 8–10 months). The rainfall also has a marked effect. Heavy rains will cause the chlorate to be washed through the soil much more quickly than when there is little rainfall. Depending on the prevailing conditions then, the soil may take anything from 4 to 12 months to become completely clear of the chemical.

THE USES OF SODIUM CHLORATE

As stated earlier, sodium chlorate is expensive and, therefore, not to be recommended on a large scale except under very exceptional circumstances. On a small scale, however, it has many uses, which may be grouped as follows:

(a) Controlling infestations of weeds on uncultivated land such as paths, drives, rubbish heaps, car-parks, hard tennis courts, railways, neglected corners and waste places. It should not be used for this purpose amongst inflammable materials, e.g. in areas used for the storage of petrol and oil, in timber yards or saw mills, in stack-yards, etc.

(b) Controlling large infestations or patches of weed in cultivated land which cannot be controlled more economically by cultural methods.

(c) Spot treatment.

When using the weedkiller on paths which run between

areas of cultivated land it should be kept sufficiently far
from the edge of the path so that it does not spread into
growing crops. A margin of a foot between the chlorate
and the cultivated land should be sufficient. Where it is
used on arable land the best time for application is the
early Autumn. Not only is this a good time for controlling
the weeds, but usually the chemical is sufficiently clear
of the soil by the Spring to allow a crop to be grown.
Suitable Spring crops for following Autumn application
of chlorate are oats, peas, cabbage and late maincrop
potatoes, while tomatoes, barley, turnips and beet of all
kinds should be avoided.

As a spot treatment sodium chlorate is unsurpassed: only
very small quantities of it are required which can be applied
as a solid or concentrated liquid. In the solid form a small
pinch of the chemical between thumb and forefinger applied
to the crown of the weed is usually sufficient. A good method
of applying it in solution is to use a metal (NOT wood) meat
skewer. The skewer is dipped into the strong solution (e.g.
1 oz. dissolved in ¼ pint of water) of chlorate and then pushed
into the crown of the weed. Applied in this way sufficient of
the liquid is carried on the skewer to kill the weed. Special
devices about the size of a walking-stick have also now been
devised for applying the weedkiller solution in small doses;
with these a 10% solution (1 lb. in a gallon of water) should be
sufficiently strong. It is sometimes recommended that the
weeds should be cut off at the crown before the chlorate is
applied, but in my experience this does not increase its
effectiveness. Provided only small doses are used sodium
chlorate can be used for spot treatment in pastures, lawns,
cereal and other crops.

Sodium chlorate can also be used in a modified form in the
Scarlett method of weed control (*see* Chapter Four). For this
the land is ploughed in Winter or early Spring and then,
before April, sodium chlorate is applied at the rate of 1½ cwt.
per acre. The land should be ploughed again about mid-
July and white mustard sown at the rate of 28 lb. per acre.
Before the seed pods form in the Autumn the mustard is rolled

and ploughed in. Two further ploughings should be given, one during the Winter and another prior to cropping in the following Spring.

The rate at which sodium chlorate is used depends on the type of weeds to be controlled. Most annuals can be controlled with 20 lb. per acre, while some very resistant perennials may require 4 cwt. per acre and others may not be controlled at all. The usual rate of application recommended for perennial weeds is 1–2 cwt. per acre. Although there is still a lack of detailed information about the amounts of chlorate required to kill different weeds, an attempt has been made to remedy this for some of the more common types in Table 10.

The weeds in Table 10 marked with an asterisk vary in their response to sodium chlorate but they can certainly be killed, including some of those stated to be resistant, by very high dressings or by spot treatment. Clumps of these weeds, e.g. Nettles in pastures, can be controlled by applying chlorate at the rate of 2–8 oz. per square yard, but it must be remembered such high dressings will render the soil useless for a long time.

Sodium chlorate is equally effective whether applied wet or dry, the choice being a matter of convenience or personal preference. When using any weedkiller the aim is to apply it evenly; this usually necessitates the application of small dressings of chlorate in solution. For these a 2% solution is very convenient. Some people prefer to apply even the higher dressings in solution because it reduces the risk of fire; in this case a 6% or 12% solution is most convenient. The strength of the solution does not matter very much, as it is the quantity of chemical applied which is important, but there is some evidence that a fairly strong solution (e.g. 12%) is better for the more resistant weeds.

The dry chemical can be applied by hand or with a thoroughly cleaned manure distributor. As a spray it can be applied with a watering-can, a knapsack sprayer or even a larger sprayer if necessary. It cannot be emphasized too much that all equipment must be thoroughly washed out after use.

TABLE 10

The Control of Weeds with Sodium Chorate

WEED	CWT. PER ACRE SODIUM CHLORATE
Annual Nettle	1/14 (10 lb.)
Bent grasses	2
Bindweeds	2
Bracken	1–2
Buttercups	½
Celandine	½
Chickweed	¼
Coltsfoot	1½
Couch	2
Creeping Thistle	2*
Docks	R*
Ground Elder	R
Groundsel	½
Knotgrass	1
Ox-eye Daisy	1½
Plantains	½
Ragwort	1
Sorrels	R*
Stinging Nettle	2*
Wild Chervil	1½
Wild Onion	R

R—Resistant.   * See text. p, 80

SULPHATE OF AMMONIA

Sulphate of ammonia cannot truly be described as a non-selective weedkiller; not only does it find several uses in the field of selective weed control but it is, above all else, a fertilizer. The factor deciding the category into which it will fall at any one time is the quantity used. The explanation of its weedkilling properties is still only incompletely understood. The main reason for including it in this chapter is that it is often employed as a spot treatment for killing weeds in lawns and sports grounds. For this purpose it is applied dry to the crown of the weed, about a teaspoonful being used for each treatment. Apart from being comparatively cheap there is little chance of scorching the grass around the weed as sometimes happens with sodium chlorate.

C.M.U.

The letters C.M.U. are an abbreviation for Chlorophenyl diMethyl Urea, which is the name of a chemical developed in the U.S.A. as a non-selective weedkiller and recently introduced into this country. It is too early yet to say very much about this substance, but preliminary tests are very promising. It is non-corrosive, non-inflammable, and can be manufactured as a wettable powder for application as a spray. Present reports from extensive tests suggest that it is remarkably effective against all plant life and will be useful for controlling weeds in any places where the land is not cultivated. As its effect is not known on all the common crops nor how long it will persist in the soil it cannot yet be recommended for agricultural use, but there is already a suggestion that it might find wide application as a pre-emergence treatment. The action of C.M.U. commences in the root and then works upwards through the stems to the leaves.

CHAPTER NINE

THE CONTACT SELECTIVE
WEEDKILLERS

THE first selective weedkiller to be discovered was copper sulphate. The discovery was made in the vineyards of France in the year 1896. Grape vines suffer from a number of fungus diseases which can be prevented by spraying copper sulphate in the form of either Bordeaux or Burgundy mixture. Some of the workers applying the spray noticed that although the vines were unharmed some of the weeds growing beneath the vines were killed. Following this observation it was found that by spraying copper sulphate on cereal crops, weeds, like Charlock, could be killed without harming the corn. Since that time copper sulphate has largely been superseded by more efficient chemicals, but it is interesting to note it remained unchallenged for over twenty years and even today is not entirely forgotten. Even during the last war it was used, mixed with sulphate of ammonia, for controlling Charlock and similar weeds in corn. The mixture employed consisted of 20 lb. copper sulphate and 1 cwt. sulphate of ammonia and was applied at the rate of 1–2 cwt. per acre in the early morning while the dew was still present. Since the war we have discovered that copper sulphate can also be used on field peas. The chief objection to copper sulphate is that it kills only a narrow range of weeds.

As already stated in Chapter Five the selective weedkillers at present in use in this country can be divided into two groups: Contact weedkillers and Growth Regulators. Included among the Contact weedkillers are a number of chemicals which are also fertilizers; for the sake of convenience we shall put these in a group by themselves and term them Fertilizer weedkillers. In this chapter we shall discuss the properties and use of the important chemicals in the Contact and Fertilizer groups, leaving the Growth Regulators to Chapter Ten.

At present there are six selective weedkillers in use in this country which fall into the Contact group: these are copper chloride, B.O.V., D.N.O.C., D.N.B.P., light mineral oils and T.C.A. The last one, an abbreviation for TriChlorAcetic acid, is a very recent introduction, which has yet to fully prove its worth, so we shall devote only a little space to it. It is intended for use against weed grasses such as Couch and is applied, in the form of one of its salts, either as a high-volume spray or as a spot treatment. At suitably low rates it is selective and can be used in a number of crops. At higher rates it is suggested it might replace the bare fallow, particularly where this is directed against weed grasses. As T.C.A. persists in the soil only about eight weeks, the period of the fallow could be considerably reduced and at the same time many of the expensive cultivations avoided.

COPPER CHLORIDE

Copper chloride is a blue crystalline solid which is soluble in water. Surprisingly enough, in view of the early success of copper sulphate, its usefulness as a weedkiller was not fully investigated until 1941. Copper chloride is an improvement on the sulphate in that it will kill a wider range of weeds, including Charlock, Pennycress (*Thlaspi arvensis*), Treacle Mustard (*Erysimum cheiranthoides*) and Black Bindweed (*Polygonum convolvulus*). It is most effective against weeds when weather conditions are warm and sunny. The rates of application used vary between 10 and 30 lb. per acre depending on the weed species present, the material being dissolved in water to give a high-volume spray. Wetting agents must never be included in the spray solution.

Copper chloride can be used in any of the cereal crops, except when these are undersown, when it can be employed only as a pre-sowing or pre-emergence treatment in relation to the grasses and clovers. After application the sprayer must be thoroughly washed out as the chemical is highly corrosive. The mixing of the spray solution should be done in wooden or enamelled vessels, not in those where bare metal is exposed. Like all other soluble copper salts, copper chloride is poisonous.

B.O.V.

The letters B.O.V. stand for Brown Oil of Vitriol, which is a commercial form of sulphuric acid. Although it contains only 77% of the pure acid the two terms are often used synonymously. It must be noted, therefore, that the rates of application given in this book, and usually elsewhere, are in terms of B.O.V. and not the pure acid.

B.O.V., like copper sulphate, was first investigated as a selective weedkiller in France, and, although it has been in use since the early 1920s, still has much to commend it. Not only will it kill a very wide range of weeds but it can also be used in a number of different crops including cereals, onions and leeks. Another useful property is that, although its action is improved by warm sunny conditions, B.O.V. is the most satisfactory of all the contact weedkillers for application in cold weather. The acid also acts very quickly, so rain—unless it falls within a few hours after treatment—has very little effect on it.

B.O.V. is applied at rates varying between 7 and 13 gallons per acre and is always diluted with water to give a high-volume spray. Its effectiveness against difficult weeds, such as Fat Hen, Mayweeds (*Anthemis and Matricaria spp.*), Knotgrass (*Polygonum aviculare*), Persicaria, Annual Nettle, Parsley Piert and Shepherd's Purse can be increased by including a wetting agent. Wetting agents of the soft-soap type, however, cannot be incorporated with B.O.V.

Being an acid, B.O.V. is very quickly neutralized by the chalk in the soil. This property makes the acid particularly suitable as a pre-emergence treatment and it is used as such in the case of onions, bulbs and undersown corn.

Sulphuric acid is very corrosive and only certain types of spraying machines can be used. Even these must be thoroughly washed out after use. Care must be taken, too, not to get the acid in the eyes or on the skin or clothing, as it will burn holes in all three with serious consequences! Another precaution essential to observe is that when diluting any strong acid like sulphuric, *the acid should always be poured into water*, NEVER the water into the acid. In the latter case considerable heat is evolved, which may cause the acid to spurt up into the face.

B.O.V. is usually supplied in glass carboys packed in straw in a metal basket. These are very awkward to handle, and a man, however strong, should never try to tip one by himself. Tipping of the carboy can be avoided altogether by the use of a siphon or, better still, by having a suitable suction pipe, worked from the spraying machine, to take the acid directly into the spray tank (*see* Chapter Fourteen). As stated in Chapter Eight, sulphuric acid should never be stored in the same room, or loaded on the same vehicle, as sodium chlorate.

B.O.V. will give good control of the following weeds at the rates stated:

7 *gallons per acre*

Charlock	Pennycress

10 *gallons per acre*

Annual Nettle	Spurrey
Cleavers	Treacle Mustard
Hemp Nettle	White Mustard
Shepherd's Purse	

13 *gallons per acre*

Black Bindweed	Persicaria
Knotgrass	Wild carrot

Other weeds which are controlled to a lesser, but satisfactory, extent by the higher dressings, include: Chickweed, Fat Hen, Runch, Scentless Mayweed (*Matricaria maritima*) and Speedwell.

D.N.O.C.

The letters D.N.O.C. (or sometimes D.N.C.*) are an abbreviation for DiNitro-Ortho-Cresol, which is a yellow dye originally produced as a by-product of the coal industry. The chemical is also an acid, but of quite a different type from sulphuric acid. It appears on the market in three forms, the sodium salt or unactivated D.N.O.C., activated D.N.O.C. and the amine salt. The sodium salt and activated D.N.O.C. are both largely insoluble in water and are sold as suspensions

---

* This form is now recommended by the British Standards Institution.

or pastes usually containing 3 lb. of the active material per gallon (this fact should always be confirmed from the makers' instructions). The amine salt is entirely soluble in water and is usually marketed in the solid state. The sodium salt is more selective than the activated form and, therefore, is not so effective against some weeds, particularly Cleavers, but it can be used in linseed and flax. The activity of the sodium salt can be increased by the addition of an "activator" in the form of sulphate of ammonia. This should be added to the spray solution at the rate of 10 lb. per 100 gallons. The amine salt tends to be rather unpredictable in its action but it is claimed that this objection can be overcome by the inclusion of a special penetrant. For formulations other than the amine it is necessary to use a spraying machine having an agitator, preferably of the paddle type (*see* Chapter Fourteen).

D.N.O.C. is applied at rates varying betewen 4 and 8 lb. per acre (4–6 activated forms, 6–8 unactivated forms) as a high-volume spray, although it is claimed for the amine salt that it can be used at dilutions as low as 40 or 50 gallons per acre. It will control an even larger range of weeds than sulphuric acid but its use is confined almost entirely to cereals, although under some conditions linseed and flax are also resistant. Oats tend to be somewhat susceptible and so it is advisable to spray these only when they are dry. The varieties S.147 and S.172 seem particularly susceptible and these should not be sprayed with D.N.O.C. The effectiveness of D.N.O.C. is dependent on temperature and it should not be applied when the air temperature is below 50°F. Temperatures above 55°F. are most satisfactory and above 70°F. rates of application can be reduced. D.N.O.C. should not be applied when frost is imminent or within a week to ten days of rolling.

D.N.O.C. will give a good control of the following weeds at the rates stated (rates are given in terms of unactivated D.N.O.C.—reduce rates by 2 lb./acre for activated forms):

6 lb. per acre

Charlock   Treacle Mustard
Pennycress

8 *lb. per acre*

Corn Gromwell	Mayweeds
Dead Nettle	Orache
Fat Hen	Poppy
Field Mint	Scarlet Pimpernel
Fumitory	Sowthistle (annual)
Hemp Nettle	White Mustard
Knawel	

Other weeds which can be controlled to a lesser, but satisfactory, extent with D.N.O.C. are Annual Nettle, Black Bindweed, Corn Buttercup, Cleavers, Chickweed, Cornflower (*Centaurea cyanus*), Corn Marigold, Groundsel, Ox-eye Daisy, Persicaria, Runch, Shepherd's Needle, Shepherd's Purse, Speedwell and Spurrey.

To control certain difficult weeds, such as Corn Buttercup, Corn Marigold (*Chrysanthemum segetum*), Fumitory (*Fumaria officinalis*) and Spurrey, wetting agents can be added to the spray solution except when applied to linseed, flax, and possibly oats. As might be expected from chemicals containing nitrogen, D.N.O.C. compounds have a direct stimulating effect on the crop.

Finally, D.N.O.C. has three unpleasant properties. Firstly, it is poisonous. This property is made even worse (*a*) because the material can be taken in not only through the mouth but also through the skin, and (*b*) because its effect is cumulative. For these reasons, when using weedkillers of the D.N.O.C. type, certain precautions must be strictly observed:

1. Wear protective clothing, including overall, rubber boots, rubber gloves and an eye-shield. If a simple gasmask can be worn or a gas-proof cab fixed to the tractor pulling the spraying tackle, this is a considerable advantage. Protective clothing must not be removed during hot weather. The rubber boots and gloves should be rinsed with water before they are removed and overalls washed regularly.

2. Never consume food or smoke while spraying,

wearing protective clothing, or in the field which is being sprayed. Always wash before eating or smoking. Do not leave food, cigarettes, tobacco, clothing, etc., near the spray containers or the spraying tackle.

3. Take very great care when dealing with the concentrated spray materials.

4. Thoroughly wash all vessels which have been contaminated with D.N.O.C. and do not leave containers about where unsuspecting persons or animals may find them.

5. Never walk behind the sprayer while it is operating, and do not try to clear spray nozzles by blowing through them.

6. Stop spraying if you feel ill and consult a doctor. Symptoms of D.N.O.C. poisoning are excessive thirst, headaches, sweating and sickness.

Most of the above precautions are now enforced by law under *The Agriculture (Poisonous Substances) Regulations*, 1953.*

Because of the poisoning dangers of spraying with D.N.O.C. there is much to be said for having the work done by contractors who have the necessary equipment for protecting and examining their workers.

Secondly, D.N.O.C. is inflammable. This does not usually matter because it is either in the form of a wet paste or a solution, but if tins are left with the lids off so that the paste becomes dry, the danger is a very real one. Thirdly, D.N.O.C. is a yellow dye and anything coming into contact with it, including clothing and skin, not only becomes yellow but will remain so for quite a long time.

D.N.B.P.

The letters D.N.B.P. are an abbreviation for DiNitro secondary Butyl Phenol, but are used loosely to refer to the straight chemical or its salts (i.e. phenates, e.g. Ammonium dinitro-sec-butyl phenate). D.N.B.P. is also known as

---

* Statutory Instrument 1953 No. 358 (obtainable from H.M. Stationery Office).

"dinoseb".* The chemical properties of D.N.B.P. are almost identical with those of D.N.O.C., e.g. it is a very poisonous yellow dye, and the precautions outlined in the previous section and the legal provisions of *The Agriculture (Poisonous Substances) Regulations* apply equally emphatically. It is, however, not now marketed in paste form but as a liquid to be diluted with water. At the present time a gallon of the proprietary liquid usually contains the equivalent of approximately $1\frac{1}{2}$ or 2 lb. pure D.N.B.P., but this fact should always be checked from the makers' instructions, as it may be altered from time to time.

D.N.B.P. was originally developed for use in peas, but this has now been extended to lucerne, sainfoin, clover, leys, undersown cereals except oats and, possibly, beans and strawberries (for details *see* Chapter Thirteen). This weedkiller is a fairly recent innovation and it is still too early to state exactly what weeds it will control, but there is little doubt it will kill a fair number. One thing is certain, however: to get any control at all, the weeds must be treated while they are still young and, at the latest, before they are four inches high.

The critical factor with D.N.B.P. is not so much the weed flora as the air temperature and the growth activity of the weeds. The rates of application are given in Table 11.

TABLE 11

The Rates of Application of D.N.B.P.

LB. OF D.N.B.P. EQUIVALENT PER ACRE

AIR TEMPERATURE	POOR GROWING CONDITIONS†	GOOD GROWING CONDITIONS†
Over 70°F.	$1\frac{1}{4}$	1
65°–70°F.	$1\frac{1}{2}$	$1\frac{1}{4}$
60°–65°F.	$1\frac{3}{4}$	$1\frac{1}{2}$
55°–60°F.	2	$1\frac{3}{4}$
Below 55°F.	D.N.B.P. ineffective	

* This form is now recommended by the British Standards Institution.
† See text.

The growth conditions are described in Table 11 as "poor" when the soil is dry and low in fertility, and as "good" when the soil is moist and a fair state of fertility persists. D.N.B.P. should not be applied when the air temperature is below 55°F. It is applied as a spray at high-volume rates, although when more is known about the chemical it may be possible to use dilutions as low as 50 gallons per acre.

A tentative summary of the weedkilling powers of D.N.B.P. is given in Table 12; the growth stages given are the maxima at which control can be expected, but the general rule is "the younger the better".

TABLE 12

Weeds Controlled by D.N.B.P.

WEED	GROWTH STAGE	
	Height (ins.)	True-Leaf Stage
Annual Nettle	Seed leaves only	
Black Bindweed ...	2 − 3	4 − 6
Charlock	3 − 4	6 − 8
Chickweed	1 − 2	1 − 2
Cleavers	Seed leaves only	
Fat Hen	1 − 2	1 − 2
Fumitory	1 − 2	1 − 2
Groundsel	1 − 2	1 − 2
Hemp Nettle	3 − 4	6 − 8
Knot Grass	Seed leaves only	
Pennycress	2 − 3	4 − 6
Persicaria	Seed leaves only	
Runch	2 − 3	4 − 6
Shepherd's Purse ...	2 − 3	4 − 6
Speedwell	Seed leaves only	
Treacle Mustard ...	3 − 4	6 − 8

Other weeds which may also be controlled at a young stage are Black Nightshade, Corn Buttercup, Mayweeds, Poppy and Scarlet Pimpernel.

Finally it must be emphasized again that the state of our

knowledge regarding D.N.B.P. is still very young and, there-fore, the recommendations given must only be considered as a guide, which may have to be amended as the results of more research become available. This is equally true of the light mineral oils to be considered next.

LIGHT MINERAL OILS

It has been known for a long time that oils like T.V.O. (tractor vapourizing oil) can be used as non-selective weed-killers. T.V.O., however, is not a single oil but a mixture of oils and different batches of it leaving the refineries, although they have the same volatility, may vary in the oils they contain. It has now been discovered that some batches of T.V.O. have a selective action in that they can be sprayed on carrots without damaging them. It has been stated that whether or not T.V.O. has this selective action depends on the amount of light aromatic oils it contains, but work by Blackman and Ivens* does not entirely support this view. It seems likely that the selectivity of light mineral oil depends on a number of factors besides the aromatic content; factors such as the penetration of the oil into the leaf (which in turn depends on the leaf structure of the plant and the physical properties of the oil, e.g. volatility), and the mixture of hydrocarbons making up the oil.† Nevertheless, despite our lack of precise knowledge regarding the factors determining selectivity, it has been possible to select oils especially suitable for selective weed control in carrots and a number of these are now on the market. To distinguish from T.V.O. we shall call them "proprietary oils". The use of these oils has now been extended to include parsnips, and possibly certain seed-lings of forest trees (*see* Chapter Thirteen). The proprietary oils have not ousted T.V.O. altogether, however, and this can still be used, provided two warnings are heeded:

1. Not all batches of T.V.O. are selective and so it is essential to ascertain this first of all by treating a small

* *Agriculture* (1949), 56; 2; 58–61. G. E. Blackman and G. W. Ivens.
  † For further details see *World Crops* (1951), 3; 10; 399–401. G. E. Barnsley.

Photograph by H. W. Gardner

3a. The control of charlock in cereals using M.C.P.A. Treated and untreated strips

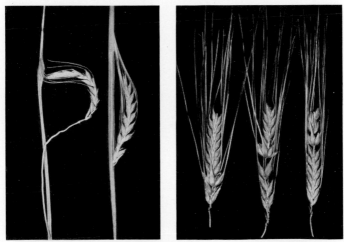

Photographs by E. C. Large and W. A. R. Dillon Weston

3b and 3c. "Bowed ears" (b) and "Tweaked ears" (c) in wheat, caused through spraying too early with growth-regulator type weed killers

Photograph by H. W. Gardner

4a. The control of buttercups in grassland using 3 lb. per acre of M.C.P.A. applied as a spray

Photograph by The Sports Turf Research Institute

4b. The control of weeds in sports turf. The grass on the left-hand side of the string has been sprayed with 2, 4-D at the rate of 6 lbs/acre following pre-treatment with nitro-chalk

patch of the crop with the batch of oil you intend to use.

2. T.V.O. may leave a taint if applied too near harvest, and for this reason must not be used on carrots intended for bunching.

Both T.V.O. and proprietary oils are highly inflammable and the same precautions must be adopted for their use and storage as with fuel oils. Obviously, operators should not smoke while handling or applying them, and spraying should not be carried out on very hot days or when the crop is wet.

Spray machines should be equipped with oil-resisting washers and hoses.

Light oils are usually applied at a rate of 60–80 gallons per acre, but in warm sunny conditions where weeds are in the seedling stage, this can be reduced to 40 gallons per acre. Wetting agents are not necessary with oils. To obtain satisfactory weed control with light oils they must be applied when the weeds are very young, preferably before the two true-leaf stage is reached.

A tentative list of weeds that can be controlled with light oils is given below:

Annual Nettle	Poppy
Charlock	Scentless Mayweed
Chickweed	Shepherd's Purse
Dead Nettle	Speedwell
Fat Hen	Spurrey
Fumitory	and some Grasses
Orache	

Fertilizer Weedkillers

This section is devoted to chemicals which, because they are best known as fertilizers, can be called fertilizer-weed-killers. Probably the most important of these is sulphate of ammonia, but the use of this material as a weedkiller has already been explained in Chapters Three, Eight and at the beginning of this chapter. Two other fertilizer weedkillers worthy of mention are calcium cyanamide and kainit.

G

CALCIUM CYANAMIDE

Calcium cyanamide is a fertilizer containing just over 20% of nitrogen and about 20% of free lime and chalk. It is usually marketed as a very fine powder, which is the form to use for weedkilling purposes. It is very effective against Charlock and Runch but will control other weeds including Annual Nettle, Chickweed, Cornflower, Fat Hen, Groundsel, Shepherd's Purse and Speedwell. For it to be really successful the weeds must be treated at a young stage and when wet with dew.

Although a fertilizer, calcium cyanamide contains certain chemicals which are injurious to plant life, but these are soon rendered ineffective when the material is incorporated into the soil. For this reason the fertilizer is usually distributed on the soil about a week before sowing seeds or transplanting. Used at this time it will kill many seedling weeds present in the seed-bed as well as those which germinate subsequently and thus reduce the weediness of the following crop. Apart from this it can also be used in asparagus, as a top dressing for cereals, grassland, and onions, and also as a pre-emergence treatment in certain bulb crops.

To control weeds in cereals and grassland it should be appled at $1\frac{1}{2}$ cwt. per acre in the Autumn or Spring while the dew is on the weeds. There may be some scorching of the crop foliage but this will recover after a few days. Where it is used in pastures the grass should not be grazed until after there has been sufficient rain to wash the cyanamide into the soil. In asparagus beds the fertilizer can be distributed over the ground at a rate of 6 cwt. per acre in late April or early May, and should control the weeds during the cutting period. Application should not be made when the asparagus shoots are just coming through the ground. When cyanamide is used in this way no further dressings of nitrogen fertilizers are required. Beds of narcissus, iris and gladiolus bulbs can be treated with 4–6 cwt. per acre of cyanamide any time in the period shortly after planting until just before the shoots appear above the surface. As a top dressing for onions it should be applied at 3 cwt. per acre when onions are from 3–4 inches high.

Cyanamide is an unpleasant material to handle, but can

be applied with ordinary fertilizer distributors and dusting machines. If applied by hand the hands and arms should first be covered with vaseline.

With the recent tremendous advances in the use of selective weedkillers there is a tendency for the older ones to be overlooked but calcium cyanamide is still worthy of consideration. It should be remembered that, in addition to any destruction of weeds, the cyanamide will have a fertilizing value on the crop equivalent to about 80% of its weight of sulphate of ammonia.

KAINIT

Low-analysis potash salts are still often bought under the old name of "Kainit", though the material for which the name is properly used is no longer marketed. To be successful as a weedkiller it must be applied in a finely divided state and the weeds must be at a young stage and preferably covered with dew. It can be used in cereals and at 4–6 cwt. per acre will control Charlock, Runch and other weeds. There is little to commend its use, however, except where cereal crops are known to be deficient in potash and are, therefore, likely to respond to it as a fertilizer.

CHAPTER TEN

THE GROWTH—REGULATOR WEEDKILLERS

THE first two weedkillers of the growth-regulator type were developed during the Second World War. Since that time many other similar materials have been tested, but up to the time of writing only one other, 2,4,5-T, has appeared on the market. The original two still remain the most important; of these M.C.P.A. was largely developed in this country and 2,4-D in the U.S.A. Although they are both very similar we will consider them separately.

M.C.P.A.

The letters M.C.P.A. are an abbreviation for 2 Methyl 4 ChloroPhenoxyAcetic acid. As a weedkiller it is usually used as the sodium salt, although recently the potassium salt has also been introduced. It is marketed both in dust and spray forms. At the present time dust forms usually contain 1 or 2 lb. of acid equivalent per cwt. and are sold ready for use. The concentrated solution sold for application as a spray contains 3 or 4 lb. of acid per gallon in most of its proprietary forms and requires to be diluted. These concentrations may not apply to all the commercial products and in any case they may be altered at any time; it is important, therefore, to be guided by the makers' instructions.

Spray forms of M.C.P.A. may be applied at either low or high-volume rates, depending on the machinery available and the crops to be treated. The low-volume rates can be as low as 5 gallons per acre, but in the writer's opinion it is wiser to err on the side of caution and not go below 10 gallons per acre. Application of M.C.P.A. dusts can be performed either by hand or with a manure distributor; it is not necessary to purchase special equipment.

M.C.P.A. is non-inflammable, non-corrosive and non-poisonous. Where it is applied to pastures there is no danger to stock, except, perhaps, where Ragwort is present. Ragwort is a poisonous weed which is not normally eaten by stock, but after treatment with growth-regulator weedkillers it seems to become more palatable. When pastures containing a dangerous amount of Ragwort have been sprayed it is wisest to keep stock out until the Ragwort plants have turned brown. Most of the precautions necessary in using M.C.P.A. arise from the fact that very minute quantities can do considerable damage to susceptible crops. For this reason, vessels which have contained the chemical should be thoroughly washed out after use, and spraying or dusting should not be carried out where winds are likely to blow the material on to surrounding crops. Very particular care is needed near glasshouses or when lawns, with surrounding flower-beds, are being treated. Commercial preparations of M.C.P.A. usually have an odour which, even if not considered strong or unpleasant, is very penetrating. Because of this they should not be stored in the same room as foodstuffs or clothes.

M.C.P.A. will not control quite such a wide range of arable weeds as sulphuric acid or D.N.O.C., but it does control some weeds, particularly perennials, against which the contact weedkillers have little effect, e.g. Corn Buttercup, Hoary Pepperwort (*Cardaria draba*), Knapweed and Shepherd's Needle. At the same rates, the spray form is more effective than the dust. M.C.P.A. can be used on a number of crops including cereals, linseed, flax, grassland, lawns, and peas. Provided there is no rain for a few hours after application the weather has very little effect on the action of M.C.P.A. The material remains active in the soil for about 6–8 weeks or longer.

M.C.P.A. gives a good control of the following weeds at the rates stated. The rates have to be increased at least half as much again when using dusts.

$\frac{3}{4}$–1 *lb. acid equivalent per acre*

Charlock	Pennycress

2 *lb. acid equivalent per acre*

Creeping Buttercup	Tall Buttercup
Hoary Pepperwort	Treacle Mustard
Ribwort	White Mustard
Runch	

Other weeds which can be controlled to a lesser, but satisfactory, degree with the higher rates of application are:

Bulbous Buttercup	(*Ranunculus bulbosus*)
Catsear	(*Hypochaeris radicata*)
Common Rush	(*Juncus effusus*)
Corn Buttercup	
Cornflower	
Dandelion	
Fumitory	
Hawksbeard	(*Crepis spp.*)
Hemp Nettle	
Knapweed	
Orache	
Plantain (Broad-leaved)	(*Plantago major*)
Scarlet Pimpernel	
Selfheal	
Shepherd's Needle	
Shepherd's Purse	
Spear Thistle	
Vetch	(*Vicia sativa*)

2,4-D

The abbreviation 2,4-D is a shortened form of 2,4-Dichloro phenoxyacetic acid; another abbreviation sometimes encountered is D.C.P.A., but this has the disadvantage of being too easily confused, particularly in speech, with M.C.P.A. It is used in three forms: the sodium salt, the amine salt and as various esters. The sodium salt is the least active of the three against weeds and is little used in proprietary products. The amine salt is the most popular of the three forms, being employed in the bulk of the commercial preparations in this country, and is intermediary in selectivity between the sodium salt and the esters. The ester forms are the most drastic in their action against weeds but the least selective; they can, therefore, often be applied at lower rates than the other two. All three forms are sold chiefly as sprays, although dust preparations are on the market.

The chemical is very similar to M.C.P.A., and most of the remarks made about that material regarding its properties, methods of application, precautions and odour, apply equally to 2,4-D and will not be repeated. Here we shall confine ourselves to a discussion of the differences between the two materials.

2,4-D cannot be used in quite so many crops as M.C.P.A. It cannot be used in flax and peas, its use in oats is not advised and considerable care must be exercised when applying it to linseed. There is a possibility, however, of its being used on strawberries. 2,4-D can be applied at low volumes. For weed control on lawns, 2,4-D is particularly useful, especially where Dandelions and Daisies predominate.

While it controls most of the same weeds as M.C.P.A., 2,4-D is probably a little more effective against:

Annual Nettle	Knawel
Common Rush	Lesser Bindweed
Corn Gromwell*	Plantain (Broad-leaved)
Daisy	Ragwort
Dead Nettle*	

The esters are also useful for killing some woody plants and for this purpose are often combined with 2,4,5-T.

On the other hand, M.C.P.A. tends to be more effective against Creeping and Tall Buttercups, Creeping Thistle, Hemp Nettle, Horsetails, Runch and Shepherd's Needle.

With the addition of those marked with an asterisk above the list of weeds shown earlier as controlled by M.C.P.A. can also be used for 2,4-D.

As with M.C.P.A., weather has little effect on 2,4-D and virtually none at all on the ester formulations. 2,4-D only remains active in the soil for about two weeks.

2,4,5-T

The latest addition to the selective weedkillers is a growth regulator called 2,4,5-Trichlorophenoxyacetic acid. It is marketed as an amine salt or in the form of esters and is very similar to 2,4-D. Its main use is in the control of woody growths such as Brambles (*Rubus spp.*), Wild Roses (*Rosa spp.*), Hawthorn (*Crataegus spp.*) and Broom (*Sarothamnus scoparius*). For this purpose it is sometimes sold in combination with 2,4-D. It remains effective in the soil for a much longer period than 2,4-D. As yet, however, it is too early to make any real assessment of the usefulness of 2,4,5-T.

CHAPTER ELEVEN

A CROP'S-EYE VIEW OF SELECTIVE WEEDKILLERS

1. AGRICULTURAL CROPS

WHEN deciding on the best selective weedkiller to use in any particular set of circumstances, the first consideration must be the crop. Only in the most desperate circumstances is it worth sacrificing a crop for the sake of controlling weeds, therefore it is essential to choose a weedkiller to which the crop is resistant. In this chapter and Chapter Twelve we shall discuss the use of selective weedkillers from the point of view of the crops in which they can be used.

CEREALS

During recent years there has been a tendency to develop special weedkillers for use in particular crops, e.g. D.N.B.P. for peas, and Light Oils for carrots. Prior to this, weedkillers were primarily developed for use in cereals and only subsequently were uses found for them in other crops. Thus all the earlier selective weedkillers—copper sulphate, copper chloride, B.O.V. and M.C.P.A.—can be used quite safely in all the Winter and Spring cereal crops, i.e. wheat, barley, oats, rye. D.N.O.C. and 2,4-D were also originally developed to control weeds in cereals and are still employed for this purpose, but during the last few years a number of cases of damage have been reported from using them in oats. The oat varieties S.147 and S.172 seem particularly susceptible to D.N.O.C., and its use on these is best avoided altogether, but with other varieties it is usually sufficient to see that they are in a thoroughly dry condition when sprayed. In the case of 2,4-D it is safest not to use this on oats. It has been thought for some time that certain varieties of Spring barley are also susceptible. Opinions are divided on this point, but recent work would suggest that, provided the main barley plant has six leaves and has produced at least two tillers, there is little likelihood of its being damaged. Apart from oats, the cereals are also resistant to D.N.B.P., but unless the crop is undersown there is nothing to recommend its use.

The time of application of weedkillers to cereals is important. In the case of the growth regulators application should not be made until the plants have six leaves and have tillered. This is also a useful standard to adopt for most of the contact weedkillers, although, provided the plants have tillered, earlier spraying may be possible. Using B.O.V., however, spraying can be carried out with advantage at the three- or four-leaf stage; indeed it has been shown that applying B.O.V. at the six-leaf stage or later can cause a depression in yield. Treatment with weedkillers should cease when it is obvious the ear is beginning to form (i.e. the "boot" stage). In the case of the growth regulators, applying them outside the permitted period may cause various ear distortions known as "bowed ears", "bunched ears" and "tweaked ears"* (*see* Plate 3b and c). Bowed ears occur in barley and are caused by the awns being trapped in the last leaf and the continued growth of the stem forcing the ear out of the leaf-sheath into a "bow" shape. In the cases of bunched and tweaked ears the spikelets, instead of being spread out evenly along either side of the stem, are either "bunched" together or grouped in clusters leaving bare spaces of stem between them. In oats spraying at the wrong time causes irregular branching and "blasting" of the panicle (i.e. presence of empty spikelets which are white and shrivelled).

After the safe stage has been reached, the earlier cereals can be treated the better, as this ensures not only a greater control of weeds, but also least damage to the crop by the wheels of implements. Spraying with D.N.O.C. should not be carried out within seven to ten days of rolling. In cereal crops any of the rates of application recommended in Table 13 are permissible. Low-volume application may only be employed when applying the growth regulators, and a minimum dilution of 10 gallons is suggested, although most low-volume machines will apply as little as 5 gallons per acre.

* For a full description see *Jour. of Agric. Sci.* (1951), 41; 4; 338–49. E. C. Large and W. A. R. Dillon Weston.

UNDERSOWN CEREALS

The control of weeds by selective weedkillers in under-sown cereals can be approached in one of three ways:

(a) Treatment of cover crop before undersowing.
(b) Pre-emergence treatment of the grasses and clovers.
(c) Direct spraying of the cover crop and undersown seeds.

Treatment before undersowing can be applied when the grasses and clovers are to be sown after the cereal cover crop has emerged and really aims at providing the seeds with a clean seed bed. To be used for this purpose the weedkiller must be one of a type which is quickly destroyed in the soil and which will not harm the cereal cover crop. These considerations limit the choice of materials to copper chloride, B.O.V. and D.N.O.C. D.N.O.C. should be applied about a week and copper chloride and B.O.V. at least three days before the seeds are sown. The normal precautions regarding the cereal crop must, of course, be observed.

The chemicals which can be used for pre-emergence treatment of undersown grasses and clovers are copper chloride and B.O.V. Only undersown seeds which have been drilled (as opposed to broadcast) should be treated in this way, and spraying should take place within seven days of sowing. Again, of course, the method is only applicable to seeds which are sown after the cover crop has emerged.

For the direct spraying of undersown cereals either D.N.B.P. or the growth regulators can be considered. The use of D.N.B.P. is quite straightforward provided the conditions for its use in both cereals and clover crops are observed. Application should not be carried out before the cereal plants have six leaves and are tillering or before the grasses are tillering and the clovers have reached the two to three true-leaf stage. D.N.B.P. should not be used on undersown oats.

The question of the direct spraying of undersown cereals with growth regulators has been a topic of debate for quite a long time. In some parts of the country, e.g. north-east Scotland, the practice is already well established, whereas in other parts, e.g. south-east England, it is still regarded with some suspicion. This difference should not be attributed to the idiosyncrasies of the inhabitants of the particular areas. It is far more probable that the differing climatic conditions have a bearing on the problem. Some guidance, however, can be given to farmers who wish to try this method. Firstly the best growth regulator to use varies with the dominant type of clover present in the seed mixture. Where red clover is the dominant species then a weedkiller based on M.C.P.A. is best used, but where white clover is dominant then one based on an amine formulation of 2,4-D is to be preferred. In the case of S.100 and wild white clover, however, the extra reduction in clover due to using M.C.P.A. is hardly likely to be important when one remembers the amazing powers of recovery of these varieties. Secondly the undersown clovers should not be sprayed until they have two true-leaves (i.e. trifolate ones). To sum up, then, there is some risk in spraying undersown crops with M.C.P.A. and 2,4-D, but where these crops are sufficiently weedy to justify spraying, the risk is probably well worth taking.

PERMANENT GRASSLAND

The discovery that clovers were somewhat resistant to M.C.P.A. and 2,4-D opened a new and wide field of usefulness for these chemicals in the control of weeds in permanent pasture. Both materials have since been found very effective for this purpose and where a very mixed flora of weeds is present there is little to choose between them. The two materials are not entirely synonymous in their effects, however, and in the case of some weeds one or the other of them may be the more advantageous. For example, where Buttercups and Thistles predominate, M.C.P.A. is slightly better, but in the case of Dandelions, Daisies and possibly Ragwort, 2,4-D is to be preferred. There is also some evidence that 2,4-D does less damage to clovers, but in neither case is the damage serious and the clovers recover fairly quickly.

The treatment of grassland is best delayed until as many as possible of the weeds are in the flower-bud stage. Not only are the weeds most susceptible at this time, but it has been

shown in experiments at the Hertfordshire Institute o.
Agriculture that the longer spraying is delayed in the Spring,
the less damage is done to the clovers (*see* Table 13).

TABLE 13

Experiment showing the effect on Clover of M.C.P.A.
applied at different times

NUMBER OF OCCURRENCES OF CLOVER PLANTS IN TWENTY
THROWS OF A SIX-INCH FRAME*

| | *M.C.P.A. APPLIED IN* | | | *NO APPLICATION* |
	Middle of Mar.	*Middle of April*	*Late May*	
Block A	40	74	86	73
Block B	136	119	165	190
Average	88	96	126	132
Percentage reduction due to M.C.P.A. treatment ...	33·4	27·3	4·6	0

* For details see *Agriculture* (1950), 57; 8; 359–64. S. J. Willis.

On no occasion should more than 2 lb. per acre of either
M.C.P.A. or 2,4-D or their equivalent be used in grassland.
When spraying, either high- or low-volume dilutions may be
employed. Although low-volume sprayers will apply as little
as 5 gallons per acre, a minimum dilution of 10 gallons per
acre is suggested particularly with the ester form of 2,4-D.

Some farmers have questioned whether the spraying or
dusting of pastures against weeds is justified economically.
Certainly it is difficult to produce figures to demonstrate the
value of weed control in pastures, although, in addition to
those of the present writer already quoted in Chapter One,
experiments by Halliday & Templeman* have suggested

* *Emp. J. Exp. Agric.* (1951), 19; 74; 104–12. D. J. Halliday and
W. G. Templeman.

that, given a few months to recover, permanent pasture and well-established leys do give increased yields of useful herbage after weeds have been controlled by the growth regulators. There is another point, however, which is worth making here. In my own experiments the weed control achieved on treated plots has been easily discernible five years later; thus it would seem a spraying or dusting every five years should be ample to keep weeds in check, particularly when combined with good pasture management (*see* Chapter Three). With the advent of the low-volume sprayer the cost of spraying is already very small, but if this is spread out over a five-year period the "cost per acre per year" is so trivial as to be justified almost on the grounds of tidiness alone. Even without figures to prove it, there can be little doubt the farmer "stands to gain" in many ways from the control of pasture weeds.

LEYS, CLOVER, LUCERNE, SAINFOIN

After they have been down for about three years or over, leys can be treated as permanent grassland, but before that time they must be included in the same class as clover, lucerne (alfalfa) and sainfoin. The only weedkiller that can be used in these crops is D.N.B.P. Even with this material, until we know more about it, certain precautions must be observed; these are:

(*a*) Clover must have reached the two to three TRUE-leaf (i.e. leaves typical of the mature plant) stage, and lucerne and sainfoin the three true-leaf stage, before being treated.

(*b*) There should be three clear days of dry weather before spraying when leaf surfaces will be sufficiently hard to withstand the chemical.

(*c*) If spraying is attempted when the crops are wet, they must be considerably more mature than the stage given in (*a*).

The D.N.B.P. should be applied at a rate of 1 to 2 lb. per acre, according to weather and growth conditions (*see* Chapter Nine), diluted in 80 to 100 gallons of water.

FIELD PEAS AND PEAS FOR CANNING AND DRYING

D.N.B.P. was primarily developed for use as a weedkiller in peas and is employed chiefly in this crop. The peas should be sprayed when they are between 3 and 12 inches high and preferably before they are 8 inches high. The amount applied varies between 1 and 2 lb. per acre, according to weather and growth conditions (*see* Chapter Nine), and must be diluted with at least 60 gallons of water. Peas of the canning type are more susceptible to D.N.B.P. than field peas or those intended for drying, and greater care is required.

M.C.P.A., in the dust form, can also be used on peas. The treatment is a little uncertain and should only be used in an emergency. Two pounds per acre of M.C.P.A. or its equivalent can be applied, but one is preferable. The spray forms of M.C.P.A. should not be used, nor should any form of 2,4-D.

Another weedkiller that can be used quite safely in peas is copper sulphate. Applied at 20 lb. per acre dissolved in 40 to 100 gallons of water, this will effectively kill Charlock and some other weeds without damaging the crop.

The economics of spraying peas are important. D.N.B.P. usually gives a useful increase in the crop yield while M.C.P.A. gives only a small increase and occasionally a depression in yield. Tractor hoeing of peas, on the other hand, usually increases the yield as much as spraying with D.N.B.P. at about only a tenth of the cost,* particularly when the spraying is done by contract. Thus, in the case of peas, the old methods, where they are practicable, are still superior to the new!

LINSEED AND FLAX

From a botanical standpoint linseed and flax are the same plant, but economically the difference between them is that linseed is grown for its seed and flax for its stem, from the fibre of which linen is manufactured. Linseed is a notoriously dirty crop, and it was a relief during the war years to discover it was resistant to weedkillers of the growth-regulator type. The crop is more resistant to M.C.P.A. than to 2,4-D, and whereas it can be treated with 2 lb. per acre of the former it

---

* See *Pea Growers Handbook*. Published by Home Grown Threshed Peas Joint Committee.

will only, with certainty, survive 1 lb. per acre of the latter. The esters of 2,4-D should never be used on linseed. The stage of growth of this crop is very important, and it should only be treated while between 4 and 12 inches high. Only high-volume rates of application are permissible.

Copper chloride can also be used on linseed provided the crop is between 4 and 12 inches high and no more than 10 lb. per acre of copper chloride are used dissolved in 100 gallons of water. At this concentration, however, copper chloride will kill only a very limited range of weeds.

Although they do not upset the seed formation in linseed, the growth regulators do seem to have a bad effect on the production of fibre in the stem of flax. For this reason 2,4-D cannot be used at all in flax, and M.C.P.A. only to the extent of 1 lb. per acre. Application should be made when the flax is between 4 and 6 inches high, and only high-volume dilution of 80–100 gallons per acre can be used.

FIELD BEANS

No completely satisfactory selective weedkiller for use in field beans has yet been discovered. D.N.B.P. can be used but there is an element of risk. The crop would seem to be most resistant between the seedling stage and when it is 2 inches high. The weedkiller should be applied at a rate of 1 to 2 lb. per acre, according to weather and growth conditions (*see* Chapter Nine), diluted with 80–100 gallons of water.

A summary of the uses of selective weedkillers in agricultural crops is given in Table 14.

TABLE 14

The Use of Selective Weedkillers in Agricultural Crops

Crop	*COPPER CHLORIDE lb./acre*	*B.O.V. Gal./acre*	*D.N.O.C. lb./acre*	*D.N.B.P. lb./acre*	*M.C.P.A. lb./acre*	*2, 4-D lb./acre*	*2, 4-D ESTER lb./acre*	*Stage of growth of crop*
Barley, Spring ...	10–30	7–13	6–8	1–2	$\frac{3}{4}$–2*	$\frac{3}{4}$–2*	$\frac{3}{4}$–1$\frac{1}{2}$*	After six-leaf stage to ear formation.
,, Winter ...	10–30	7–13	6–8	1–2	$\frac{3}{4}$–2*	$\frac{3}{4}$–2*	$\frac{3}{4}$–1$\frac{1}{2}$*	After six-leaf stage to ear formation.
Beans	—	—	—	1–2?	—	—	—	Seedling to 3 in. high.
Clover	—	—	—	1–2	—	—	—	After 2–3 true-leaf stage.
Flax	—	—	—	—	$\frac{3}{4}$–1	—	—	Between 4–6 in. high.
Linseed	10	—	—	—	$\frac{3}{4}$–2	$\frac{3}{4}$–1	—	Between 4–12 in. high.
Lucerne (Alfalfa)	—	—	—	1–2	—	—	—	After three true-leaf stage.
Oats, Spring ...	10–30	7–13	6–8	—	$\frac{3}{4}$–2*	—	—	After six-leaf stage to ear formation.
,, Winter ...	10–30	7–13	6–8	—	$\frac{3}{4}$–2*	—	—	After six-leaf stage to ear formation.
Peas	?	—	—	1–2	1?	—	—	Between 4–12 in. high.
Permanent Grassland	—	—	—	—	1–2*	1–2*	1–2*	—
Rye	10–30	7–13	6–8	—	$\frac{3}{4}$–2*	$\frac{3}{4}$–2*	$\frac{3}{4}$–2*	After six-leaf stage to ear formation.
Sainfoin	—	—	—	1–2	—	—	—	After three true-leaf stage.
Wheat, Spring ...	10–30	7–13	6–8	1–2	$\frac{3}{4}$–2*	$\frac{3}{4}$–2*	$\frac{3}{4}$–2*	After six-leaf stage to ear formation.
,, Winter ...	10–30	7–13	6–8	1–2	$\frac{3}{4}$–2*	$\frac{3}{4}$–2*	$\frac{3}{4}$–2*	After six-leaf stage to ear formation.

* Low-volume spraying permissible. ? An element of risk in this treatment.

CHAPTER TWELVE

A CROP'S-EYE VIEW OF SELECTIVE WEEDKILLERS

2. HORTICULTURAL CROPS

AS STATED in the previous chapter, most of the selective weedkillers were primarily intended for use in cereal crops, and in so far as they have any other uses, these have been discovered subsequently. The reason for this is that the selectivity of the chemicals employed as weedkillers is largely between monocotyledons and dicotyledons (*see* Chapter Five). It is not surprising then that selective weedkillers have been used less widely in horticulture than in agriculture, and even now (despite the introduction of weedkillers, like the light oils, suited only for use in market garden crops) have rarely reached headline status in the minds of practising horticulturists. Nevertheless, the use of selective weedkillers in horticulture is expanding and the results of present research work suggest their scope may be further increased. In this chapter we shall consider the horticultural crops in which selective weedkillers are already or may soon be in use.

LAWNS

The use of the weedkillers of the growth-regulator type for the control of weeds in lawns must be considered the major invasion of selective herbicides into horticultural practice. The growth regulators are ideal for this purpose, firstly because grasses are very resistant to them and, secondly, because of their ability to kill many perennial weeds. Both M.C.P.A. and 2,4-D, can be used very successfully, but in many cases 2,4-D is perhaps slightly the more effective. M.C.P.A., however, is to be preferred where Buttercups and Thistles are the chief weeds.

A rate of 2 lb. per acre of acid equivalent is sufficient for most lawn weeds although, occasionally, 4 lb. per acre may be required to control the more resistant ones. When 4 lb. per acre is to be used, this is better applied as two dressings of 2 lb. per acre, separated by an interval of two or three weeks, than as a single dressing. The effectiveness of the weedkillers can often be increased by giving a top dressing of nitrogen (e.g. as sulphate of ammonia) a fortnight before application.

The best time for applying M.C.P.A. and 2,4-D is probably when the weeds are in the flower-bud stage, as in pastures, but as, owing to constant mowing, the weeds are rarely able to produce buds, this time is difficult to ascertain. The best recommendation is to apply the weedkiller in the Spring when the weeds are in active growth, i.e. between April and June.

Application of the weedkillers can be made with a fine-rosed watering-can, a knapsack sprayer or, in the case of larger areas such as playing fields and golf fairways, with an ordinary spraying machine. When using a watering-can it must be thoroughly washed out afterwards as even slight traces of the growth regulators can do serious damage to cultivated plants. A good idea is to keep a watering-can to be used only for this and kindred purposes, but if you have such a can do not keep it in a glasshouse, or even take it into one. Knapsack sprayers, too, should be thoroughly cleaned out after applying weedkillers, in case they are also used for spraying insecticides and fungicides on to crops. In the dust form weedkillers can be applied by hand or with a manure distributor. The first cut of grass taken after an application of either M.C.P.A. or 2,4-D should not be used directly as a mulch on herbaceous borders and the like, but should be composted.

Newly laid turf should not be treated for six months and freshly sown grass should not be treated in its first year of growth. Where there are only a few weeds in lawns it is more economical to kill them by spot treatment. The growth regulators can also be employed for this purpose using a solution containing 1 oz. of acid equivalent per gallon of water. Each weed should be thoroughly wetted with the solution. Sodium chlorate and sulphate of ammonia can also be used for the spot treatment of weeds in lawns (*see* Chapter Eight).

The old method for controlling weeds in lawns was with the use of lawn sands. These should be applied two or three times at fortnightly intervals during the growing season at a rate of 4 oz. per square yard. (For further details *see* Chapter Three.)

ONIONS AND LEEKS

In onions and leeks weeds can be controlled selectively with B.O.V. In the case of onions it can either be used as a pre-emergence treatment or in the growing crop. Because onion seeds take a comparatively long time to germinate, the seed bed may become badly infested with weeds before the onion seedlings appear, making mechanical inter-row cultivation impossible. These weeds can be profitably controlled with B.O.V. As a pre-emergence treatment sulphuric acid can be applied at 13 gallons per acre diluted with 80–100 gallons of water and, if necessary, a wetting agent may be added. Applied to the growing crop, no more than 10 gallons per acre of B.O.V. may be used and wetting agents must not be added. When sprayed with B.O.V. the onions should be past the "loop stage", i.e. when the shoot is quite straight. At this stage the plants will be about 4 inches high. Spring onions and onions grown from sets should not be treated.

In leeks B.O.V. is not used until after setting out the plants. The acid is applied at a maximum rate of 10 gallons per acre dissolved in 100 gallons of water. Leeks must not be treated after they have been planted out for over a month.

CARROTS AND PARSNIPS

As described in Chapter Nine special proprietary light oils and, with certain precautions, some batches of T.V.O. can be used to control weeds in carrots. T.V.O. should always be tried out on a small area of the carrots before it is applied generally, but, provided it does no damage to the crop, it can be very effective.

Light oils are applied to carrots at the rate of 60–80 gallons per acre of the proprietary oil or 40–80 gallons of

T.V.O. The lower rates are used when the weather conditions are warm and sunny and the weeds are in the seedling stage. In cooler, cloudy conditions, or when the weeds are older, the higher rates must be used. When the weedkiller is applied the crop should be between the two- and four-leaf stages and the weeds as young as possible. Light oil should not be applied within three or four weeks of bunching carrots, and T.V.O. should not be used at all when carrots are to be harvested in this way.

More recent experiments have shown that light oils can also be used as a selective weedkiller in parsnips.

Forest Nurseries

Another use which has been found for light mineral oils is in the controlling of annual weeds in forest nurseries. The annual expenditure on manual weed control in such nurseries is very high and a large number of experiments have been carried out to devise methods of controlling the weeds by chemical means. Although a number of species of conifer seedlings are found to be resistant to light mineral oils the exact conditions under which the seedlings are resistant is not fully understood. Nevertheless there seems a good chance that the time when some tree seedlings can be safely sprayed is not far distant. In the meantime, however, one considerable advance has been made in the use of light mineral oils for pre-emergence spraying. Using this technique with rates of oil not exceeding 60 gallons per acre, no damage has been done to the seedlings of most hardwood and conifer species and a worth-while saving has been made in the cost of weeding.

Peas for Picking and Canning

The use of the selective weedkiller D.N.B.P. in field peas (i.e. those intended as a cattle food) and peas for drying has been described in Chapter Twelve. D.N.B.P. can also be used in peas of the garden type, but there is a much greater possibility of causing damage and some chance of delaying the picking time. Before spraying these peas, therefore, it is advisable to try out the weedkiller on a small area first, and if this is satisfactory the rest of the crop can be treated. The rates of application, etc., are as described in Chapter Twelve.

ASPARAGUS

The use of calcium cyanamide as a selective weedkiller in asparagus has already been described in detail in Chapter Ten. Experiments have also been carried out on the use of M.C.P.A. in asparagus. These have shown that asparagus in the fern stage is fairly resistant. Care must be taken not to wet the fern itself and seedlings must not be treated. Detailed recommendations cannot be given until more information is available.

BULBS

Both B.O.V. and D.N.B.P. can be used in bulbs as pre-emergence sprays, provided no part of the bulb or its shoots is showing above the ground. This means spraying will be confined to the Autumn and Winter, and in the case of D.N.B.P. to periods during the Autumn when weather conditions are suitable. B.O.V. should be used at a rate of 10 gallons per acre dissolved in 80–100 gallons of water.

STRAWBERRIES

Work in America* has suggested it may be possible to control weeds in strawberries by the use of 2,4-D. Treatment should be carried out after flowering or possibly up to two weeks before flowering. A suggested rate of application is 1 lb. per acre dissolved in 100 gallons of water. Until the results of experiments carried out in this country are available, however, it is not possible to make any firm recommendation to growers.

Another possibility for controlling weeds in strawberries which shows some promise is the use of D.N.B.P. at a rate of about 2 lb. per acre during the Autumn and Winter. Here also there is a need for more experimental confirmation.

ORCHARDS

Experiments at present being carried out in England† and abroad suggest it may be possible to use M.C.P.A. and 2,4-D for weed control in orchards, without damaging the trees. Again, however, until the full results are available it would be unwise to recommend this practice.

* See *Mass. Exp. Sta. Bull.*, No. 451, Sept. 1948. W. H. Lachman.
† See *East Malling Research Station Annual Reports*, 1949, 1950, 1951.

CHAPTER THIRTEEN

RULES FOR SUCCESSFUL SELECTIVE WEED CONTROL

SELECTIVE weedkillers are not an unerring panacea for all weed troubles, and to get the best results from them not only must their limitations be understood, but they must be used correctly. Two considerations are involved: the crop being grown and the weed flora present. In most cases the crop must take priority and this aspect has already been considered in Chapters Eleven and Twelve, but here we shall discuss some important rules for obtaining the best control of weeds.

RULE 1. CHOOSE THE MOST SUITABLE WEEDKILLER

Since the selective weedkillers do not control exactly the same range of weeds, first and foremost it is important to choose one which is effective against the particular weeds to be controlled. A list of common weeds, together with the appropriate weedkillers, is given in Table 15. Where the weeds in a crop are very mixed a chemical should be chosen which will give a satisfactory control of as many species as possible. Of course, it may not be equally effective against all the weeds, but it is better to obtain a fair degree of control of a large number than to completely kill a few and leave the rest unharmed. In the latter case those species left unharmed will have been freed from the competition of the susceptible weeds and so will have a better chance of success. There is also a lot to be said for varying weedkillers from year to year, so that those weeds missed one year are eliminated the next. Using the same weedkiller from year to year will eliminate the susceptible species, thus leaving a clear field for the resistant ones to increase and spread.

On many occasions several weedkillers will be equally effective against the weed flora concerned and equally harmless to the crop and in these cases other considerations will have to decide the issue. Firstly, the machinery available for applying the weedkiller must be considered. If a farmer or grower has no spraying machine or there is no water supply, a chemical which can be applied as a dust will be most convenient. If he has only a low-volume sprayer, it is better to choose a weedkiller he can use in his own sprayer than have to employ a contractor to apply a spray requiring high-volume dilution. Secondly, there is the nature of the material itself, whether or not it is dangerous, and if so whether the necessary equipment is available to protect the workers. Finally, such points as the possible danger to adjacent crops, the use of weedkillers already in stock, and the ease of preparation in the case of sprays, etc., will have to be taken into consideration.

RULE 2. APPLY AT THE CORRECT RATE

Having decided on the weedkiller best suited to control the weeds, it must then be applied at a rate which will kill them without harming the crop. The rates of application required to kill the various weeds are also given in Table 15. These rates are given in terms of the pure weedkilling chemical, and care must be exercised when using proprietary preparations which contain the chemical in a diluted form. For example, to apply 1 lb. of D.N.B.P., 4 pints of the proprietary material will usually be required. When applied as sprays all the weedkillers except the growth regulators are diluted to make 80 to 100 gallons of solution per acre. The growth regulators can, under most circumstances, be used at low-volume dilutions.

Applying at the correct rate means not applying at too high a rate just as much as too low a rate. If the rate used is too high, not only will weedkiller be wasted and the likelihood of damage to the crop increased, but in the case of the growth regulators, the actual weedkilling efficiency of the material may be reduced. The reason is that for the growth regulators to be effective they must be carried throughout the plant in its sap, but when too much is applied the foliage of the plant is killed and the sap transport system destroyed before the weedkiller can be carried away from the point at which it made contact with the plant.

TABLE 15

Weeds Controlled by Selective Weedkillers

Rates of copper chloride and D.N.B.P. are given in lb. per acre of the pure chemical, those of M.C.P.A. and 2,4-D in lb. of acid equivalent per acre and those of B.O.V. and light oil in gal. per acre. Rates for D.N.O.C. are in lb. per acre of the unactivated material; when using the activated form these rates should be reduced by 2 lb. per acre.

Common Name of Weed	Copper Chlor.	BOV	DNOC	DNBP	Light Oil	MCPA	2,4-D
Annual Meadow Grass	R	R	R	N	40–60†	R	R
Bedstraw	N	N	N	N	N	R	R
Bindweed:							
Black	30*	13*	8*	1–2*	N	2?	2*
Lesser	N	N	R	R	N	R	2*
Black Medick ...	N	N	N	N	N	2	2
Bladder Campion	R	R	R	R	N	R	R
Buttercup:							
Bulbous ...	N	N	N	N	N	2*	2*
Corn	R	R	8*w	1–2	N	2†	2†
Creeping ...	N	R	R	R	N	2†	2*
Tall	N	N	N	N	N	2†	2*
Catsear	N	N	N	N	N	2*	2*e
Charlock	10†	7†	6†	1–2†	60–80*	¾†	¾†
Chickweed ...	R	13*	8*	1–2*	60–80†	R	R
Mouse-ear ...	N	N	N	N	N	2	2
Cinquefoil ...	N	N	N	N	N	R	R
Cleavers	30	10†	8*	1–2*	N	R	R
Clover	?	N	N	R	R	R	R
Coltsfoot	N	R	R	R	N	R	R
Cornflower ...	R	13w	8*	N	N	2*	2*
Corn Gromwell ...	N	N	8†	N	N	R	2
Corn Marigold ...	R	13w	8*w	N	N	R	R
Cranesbills ...	N	N	8?	N	N	R	R
Daisy	N	N	N	N	N	2	2
Ox-eye	N	N	8	N	N	2	2
Dandelion ...	N	N	N	N	N	2*	2*d
Docks	R	R	R	R	N	2r	2r
Fat Hen	R	13*w	8†	1–2*	60–80†	2	2e

Common Name of Weed	Copper Chlor.	BOV	DNOC	DNBP	Light Oil	MCPA	2,4-D
Field Mint ...	N	R	8†	N	N	2	2
Fumitory	R	13w	8†w	1–2*	60–80	2*	2*
Groundsel ...	N	N	8*	1–2	60–80	2	2
Hawksbeard ...	N	N	N	N	N	4†	2†
Heartsease ...	N	N	R	R	N	2	R
Hoary Pepperwort	R	R	R	R	N	2†r	2†r
Horsetail	N	R	R	R	N	2	R
Knapweed ...	N	N	N	N	N	2*	2*
Knawel	N	N	8†	N	N	R	R
Knotgrass ...	R	13†w	8	?	N	R	R
Mayweed:							
Scentless ...	R	13*w	8*	1–2	60–80†	R	R
Stinking ...	R	13w	8†	1–2	N	R	R
Mouse-ear							
Hawkweed	N	N	N	N	N	2	2e
Mustard:							
Treacle ...	20†	10†	6†	1–2†	N	2†	2†
White	N	10†	8†	1–2†	N	2†	1†
Nettle:							
Annual ...	R	10†w	8w	?	60–80*	2	2
Dead ...	N	N	8†	N	60–80†	2	2*
Hemp ...	30*	10†	8†	1–2†	N	2*	2e
Stinging ...	R	R	R	R	R	2r	2r
Orache	R	13*w	8†?	1–2†	60–80*	2*	2*e
Parsley Piert ...	R	N	8*	N	N	?	N
Pearlwort ...	N	N	N	N	N	2?	2?
Penny Cress ...	15†	7†	6†	1–2†	N	¾†	¾†
Persicaria ...	30*	13†w	8*	R	N	R	R
Plantain:							
Ribwort ...	N	N	R	N	N	2†	2†
Broad-leaved ...	N	N	N	N	N	2*	2†
Poppy	R	R	8†w	1–2	60–80*	2	2e
Ragwort ...	N	N	N	N	N	2r?	2r*?
Runch	30*	13*	8*	1–2*	N	2†	2*
Rush, Common ...	N	N	N	N	N	2*	2*
Scabious	N	N	N	N	N	2	2
Scarlet Pimpernel	N	N	8†	N	N	2*	2*
Selfheal	N	N	N	N	N	2*	2*
Shepherd's Needle	R	13	8*	N	N	2*	2
Shepherd's Purse...	R	10†w?	8*	1–2*	60–80*	2*	2*

Common Name of Weed	Copper Chlor.	BOV	DNOC	DNBP	Light Oil	MCPA	2,4-D
Silver Weed ...	N	R	R	N	N	2	2e
Sorrels ...	N	N	N	N	N	R	R
Sow-thistle:							
Annual ...	N	N	8†	N	R	?	?
Perennial ...	R	R	R	R	R	2	2
Speedwell ...	R?	13*w?	8*?	1–2*	60–80†	R?	R?
Spurrey ...	30	10†	8*w?	R	60–80†	R?	R?
Thistle:							
Creeping ...	R	R	R	R	N	2	2
Spear ...	N	N	N	1–2†	N	2*	2*
Vetch ...	N	N	8*	R	N	2*	2*
Wild Carrot ...	N	13†	R	N	N	R?	R?
Wild Onion ...	R	R	R	N	N	R	R
Yarrow ...	N	N	N	N	N	R	R

KEY TO TABLE 15

†   Good control of weeds.
*   Fair control of weeds.
    Recommendations without asterisks or daggers only give a poor control of weeds.
d   The best time for application may be in the autumn.
e   Only used in the case of 2,4-D. Denotes that a better control can often be achieved by using an ester formulation.
N   No definite information available, except that which is of little practical use.
r   Repeat applications for 2 or 3 consecutive years where possible.
R   Weed resistant to treatment or the damage done is too small to be of practical importance. Included here are cases where the foliage of weeds is killed, but the plant remains alive to flourish again in subsequent years.
w   A wetting agent should be added to get the best effect; in the case of sulphuric acid it should not be a soft soap.
?   Results variable or treatment uncertain.
    For details of time of application see text (Rule 3).

    N.B.—Table 15 has been compiled from a large number of different sources including the writer's experience. Where the different sources are not in agreement about the effect of a weedkiller on a particular weed, the majority view has usually been taken. As a whole the Table probably underestimates the weedkilling powers of the chemicals involved.

RULE 3. APPLY AT THE RIGHT STAGE OF GROWTH

Weeds tend to increase their resistance to selective weed-killers as they get older, therefore as a good general rule they are best applied when the weeds are at a young stage of growth—in fact the younger the better. The chief exception to this rule is in the use of the growth regulators on perennial weeds, i.e. weeds of which the vegetative parts persist from year to year. For these the best general rule is to apply the growth-regulator weedkiller when the weed is in the flower-bud stage. This rule will apply very largely to the use of the weedkillers in pasture and here it has the advantage that the budding time of the weeds more or less coincides with the period when the clovers are most resistant. The reasons why perennial weeds are most susceptible at this stage are probably threefold. Firstly, in forming the flower the last food reserves are used up and, therefore, the weed is in its weakest condition. Secondly, the leaf area will be about its maximum so that the area over which the weedkiller can be absorbed will be greatest. Thirdly, the plants are in an active state of growth, so that absorption and circulation of the weedkiller will be most rapid. There are some occasions, however, when the growth regulators are not most effective at the flower-bud stage, e.g. 2,4-D on Hoary Pepperwort (*Cardaria draba*) (*see* Chapter Fourteen). Obviously we have a lot more to learn about growth regulators and so whatever theories are put forward regarding their action must only be considered interim ones while awaiting further evidence. In the case of D.N.B.P. the stage of growth at the time of application is critical, but a detailed account has already been given in Chapter Nine.

As regards Table 15 then, the recommendations there are only valid at the following growth stages:

(*a*) In the case of the growth regulators on perennial weeds—the flower-bud stage.

(*b*) In the case of the weeds controlled by D.N.B.P. (except where more detailed information is given in Chapter Nine)—the seed-leaf stage.

(*c*) In all cases, other than those given in (*a*) and (*b*)—the young-plant stage or earlier.

Apart from the weedkilling advantages of applying at the correct stage of growth there are also disadvantages in applying at a later stage of growth. Firstly, the older the weeds the more damage they will have done to the crop by competition (*see* Chapter One), and, therefore, the less value will be accrued from the use of the weedkiller. Secondly, the chances of the weeds forming seed are increased, particularly in the case of weeds such as Chickweed and Speedwell, which produce flowers in a very short time. Thirdly, as the crop gets more mature there is a greater chance of damaging it with the wheels of the machinery used for the spraying or dusting. Fourthly, and finally, when weeds in bloom are sprayed with D.N.O.C. and D.N.B.P., because of the poisoning properties of these materials, the farmer's friend the bee will be killed when visiting the flowers.

RULE 4. APPLY WHEN WEATHER CONDITIONS ARE SUITABLE

As has already been pointed out in Chapter Nine, all the contact weedkillers give their best performance in warm sunny conditions, although sulphuric acid will still give good results in dull cold weather. In the case of D.N.B.P. the air temperature is so critical as to govern the rate of application more than the weeds species to be controlled.

Rain following within a few hours of application reduces or nullifies the effectiveness of the weedkillers by washing it off the leaves of the weeds, although in the case of the ester formulations of 2,4-D and sulphuric acid this effect is reduced to a minimum. In the case of the esters this is because they adhere very firmly to the weed leaves and in the case of sulphuric acid because it acts very quickly. If weedkillers are applied in windy conditions there is a very real chance, particularly in the case of M.C.P.A. and 2,4-D, of their being blown on to susceptible crops and doing considerable damage.

The effect of calcium cyanamide, sulphate of ammonia, and copper sulphate applied dry is increased by the presence of dew on the weeds.

It is unwise at any time to apply selective weedkillers when crops are in a frosted condition.

To summarize, the rules for the successful control of weeds with selective weedkillers are:

1. Choose the most suitable weedkiller to control as many as possible of the weeds present.

2. Apply the weedkiller at the correct rate, neither above nor below.

3. Apply at the right stage of weed growth, i.e.

(a) In the case of the growth regulators, on perennial weeds, at the flower-bud stage.

(b) In the case of weeds controlled by D.N.B.P. (except where more detailed information is given in Chapter Nine), at the seed-leaf stage.

(c) In all cases, other than those in (a) and (b) above, at the young-plant stage or earlier.

4. Apply when the weather conditions are most suitable, i.e.

(a) In warm sunny conditions.

(b) When rain is not imminent.

(c) When the air is calm.

CHAPTER FOURTEEN

THE MECHANICAL APPLICATION OF WEEDKILLERS

THE mechanical equipment used for applying weedkillers may be divided into three groups:

1. Devices for applying weedkillers as spot treatments.
2. Machines for applying dusts.
3. Machines for applying sprays.

Little need be said about the first two groups. One device for applying spot treatments (the metal meat skewer) has been described in Chapter Eight. Another device which can be easily made is depicted in Fig. 7. It consists of a bottle, in which is a cork with a bent glass tube passing through it. There is also a small nick in the cork to allow air into the

Figure 7. A simple device for applying liquid spot treatments

bottle, as the liquid passes out through the glass tube. The glass tube should not have an internal diameter greater than about $\frac{1}{8}$ inch. By tipping the bottle a small jet of weedkiller can be applied to a single weed. At least one device is on the market for applying spot treatments. It is about the size of a walking-stick, but much thicker and could easily be carried by the farmer on his evening or week-end walks round the farm. The barrel of the "stick" is filled with the solution of weedkiller and treatment is made by pressing the end of the implement on to the weed.

Dusts may be applied in one of three ways: (1) by hand, (2) by manure distributor, (3) by mechanical duster. A manure distributor is quite satisfactory for the job and there is little point in buying a dusting machine purely for this purpose. The manure distributor should, of course, be thoroughly cleaned out before using it again for fertilizers. The weedkiller dusts are very light and easily carried in the wind, so care should be taken to dust only when the weather is reasonably calm, otherwise damage may be done to nearby susceptible crops.

SPRAYING MACHINES

The machines used for applying sprays are of four main types:

1. Knapsack sprayers.
2. Low-volume sprayers.
3. Sulphuric acid sprayers.
4. All-purpose sprayers.

Knapsack sprayers (*see* Plate 6b) are small machines capable of being carried on the back like a rucksack. They may either be manually or pneumatically operated. In the manual type the operator pumps the machine with one hand and directs the spray lance with the other. With the pneumatic type, pressure is first built up in the spray tank, which then forces out the spray when a valve on the lance is released; thus while actually spraying, the operator has only the lance to think about. The sprayers usually have a capacity of about

2 gallons and are employed when small areas are to be sprayed, e.g. small lawns, golf tees, clumps of weeds, experimental plots, etc. Their use is not confined to weedkillers, but may include the application of insecticides and fungicides.

Low-volume sprayers (*see* Plate 6a) are usually very simple machines for applying weedkillers at rates varying between 5 and 40 gallons per acre. They generally have a capacity of about 50 gallons, so with one filling they spray 1–10 acres according to the rate of application being used. The machine may be directly attached to the tractor or pulled as trailer and in most makes is operated from the power take-off. The rate of application is controlled by the size of the nozzles and the forward speed of the tractor.

Sulphuric acid has to be applied by machines which are specially made to stand up to its very corrosive properties. Usually the tank is made of wood (*see* Plate 5a) or metal protected with a lead or other suitable form of coating, and special nozzles are employed. The pump has also to be of a suitable type if the acid is passed through it, but this was sometimes avoided by making the machine on the pneumatic principle. Because many of the all-purpose type sprayers are now being made so that they can apply sulphuric acid, special sulphuric acid sprayers are becoming obsolete, but some are still to be found on farms where spraying has been practised for a long time. They can, of course, be used for other sprays besides B.O.V., but, because the machines are of an older type, only high-volume rates can be applied. Sprayers with wooden tanks should not be used for the growth regulators as these are absorbed into the wood, making thorough cleaning impossible.

All-purpose sprayers, as the name suggests, can be used for almost any spraying work. Often they will spray at high or low volume, high or low pressures, will apply all types of material including sulphuric acid, mineral oils, fungicides and insecticides, and can be used on ground crops or in orchards. Such machines are, of course, much dearer than the types already mentioned, and their cost may run into several hundreds of pounds.

The Construction of Spraying Machines.—It is only intended

Photograph by W. Weeks & Son Ltd.

5a. A sulphuric acid spraying machine

Photograph by Pest Control Ltd.

5b. An all-purpose spraying machine

Photograph by Kent Engineering & Foundry Ltd.

6a. A low-volume spraying machine

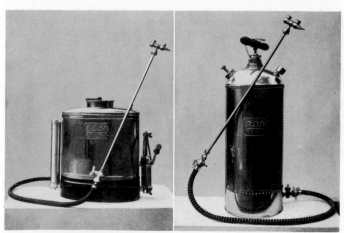

Photographs by Four Oaks Spraying Machine Ltd.

6b and 6c. Knapsack sprayers of the hand-operated (b) and
pneumatic (c) types

to give a simple outline of the construction of spraying machines here; for details of construction of any particular machine, reference should be made to the instruction book provided with it.

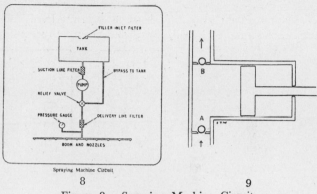

Spraying Machine Circuit

8   9

Figure 8.   Spraying Machine Circuit
By permission of the Controller of H.M. Stationery Office
Figure 9.   A Reciprocating Pump

A spraying machine consists of the following essential parts: (*a*) the tank, (*b*) the pump, (*c*) the hoses, (*d*) the boom and (*e*) the nozzles (*see* Fig. 8). In addition, other very important parts of every spraying machine are the filters.

The tank is the part which acts as a reservoir for the spray solution. In most of the modern machines it is made of metal, but wood was used in many older types. The metal should be galvanized or of a type that does not easily rust. Where the sprayer is to be used with B.O.V. the tank must be specially constructed to resist the corrosive action of the acid. The tank is provided with a "filler hole" through which it can be filled with the spray solution.

The pump may be one of two kinds, reciprocating or rotary. A reciprocating pump is illustrated very simply in Fig. 9. When the plunger is pulled out the spray is drawn in through valve "A" and when the plunger is pushed in the spray is forced out through valve "B". The rotary pump, simply illustrated in Fig. 10, is constructed of two gear wheels (hence this type is usually referred to as a "Gear Pump")

I

enclosed in a box. The wheels rotate in opposite directions as shown by the arrows, collecting spray from the inlet pipe in the spaces between the teeth and ejecting it through the outlet pipe.

The hoses are the pipes which carry the spray solution from the pump to the boom and are usually made of rubber. As rubber is damaged by oil, sprayers required to spray light

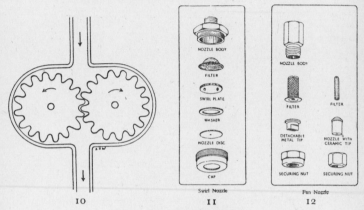

Figure 10.   A Gear Pump
Figure 11.   Swirl Nozzle
By permission of the Controller of H.M. Stationery Office
Figure 12.   Fan Nozzle
By permission of the Controller of H.M. Stationery Office

oils must be equipped with hoses made of special oil-resisting materials.

The boom is the long metal pipe which distributes the spray, brought to it by the hoses to the nozzles. So as to cover a very wide area, the boom is usually made as long as is practicably possible. As this is much too long to go through gates and travel along roads the boom is either made in three sections—a centre section which remains rigid, and two side sections which can be folded back along the sides of the spray tank—or in two halves which fold vertically. The nozzles may be fitted directly to the boom or carried on pipes, projecting from the boom, called "lances".

The nozzles are a very important part of the spraying

machine and are responsible for spreading the spray evenly over the crop in the form of small droplets, an action achieved by forcing the spray solution through a very fine orifice. The stream of droplets leaving the nozzle may form a cone shape or a fan shape, depending on the type of nozzle used, i.e. whether it is a "swirl" nozzle (Fig. 11) or a "fan" nozzle (Fig. 12). Very often, together with the pressure and the tractor speed, the size of the nozzle orifice controls the rate of application of the spray.

Because the orifice of the nozzle is very small it can easily become blocked by any small particles of dirt in the spray. For this reason the sprayer is provided with filters at various points to ensure that the spray getting through to the nozzles is dirt-free. Filters are usually provided in the filler hole, in the delivery pipe from the pump and in the nozzles themselves (*see* Figs. 11 and 12).

Most spraying machines are provided with a number of accessories of which we shall mention two, the "suction hose" and "agitators". A suction hose is used for filling the tank instead of via the filler hole. The hose is put into the source of water or spray solution and, using a suction provided by the pump, draws the water or spray into the tank. The suction hose usually has a filter over its free end. An "agitator" is a device for keeping the spray solution in the tank thoroughly mixed. It may be one of two types, mechanical or circulatory. Mechanical agitation is provided by rotating paddles incorporated in the spray tanks. The principal of circulatory agitation is that too much spray is taken from the tank by the pump and the excess is forced back, causing a continual movement of the fluid in the tank and keeping it mixed. Mechanical agitation is the more effective, even if a little more clumsy.

Filling the Tank.—The tank may either be filled with the ready-mixed spray solution or with water to which concentrated weedkiller is added separately and mixed by the agitator. Where machines have no agitator the spray should always be ready mixed when added to the tank. When mixing in the tank, half to two-thirds of the water should be added first, then the required quantity of weedkiller, and finally the rest of the water. The whole should then be thoroughly agitated. When filling with sulphuric acid, use the suction hose if possible or, if using the filler hole, have two men available to manipulate the carboy. Copper sulphate, copper chloride and the sodium salt of 2,4,-D are best dissolved in a quantity of water before being added to the tank. Take all necessary precautions when handling B.O.V. and the concentrated forms of D.N.O.C. and D.N.B.P. (*see* Chapter Nine).

The Choice of a Sprayer.—The choice in purchasing a sprayer will usually be between a low-volume and an all-purpose machine. Where a farmer has only corn crops and pastures to spray, unless he has a very large acreage his "best buy" is a low-volume sprayer. These are reasonably cheap, are very economical in their use of water and will do most of the jobs he requires. The low-volume sprayer has, however, certain disadvantages:

1. It cannot be used for spraying copper chloride, B.O.V., D.N.O.C., D.N.B.P. or light oils.
2. It cannot be used to spray M.C.P.A. and 2,4-D on linseed and flax.
3. It cannot be used for spraying some types of fungicide on potatoes.

On farms where these disadvantages are important, e.g. where a wide variety of weeds is encountered, where market gardening is carried on, etc., then a machine of the all-purpose type should be considered. All-purpose machines tend to increase in price with their universality and this point should be considered when choosing your machine. For example, a farmer who has no orchard will not require a machine which can be used for tree spraying.

For groundsmen and lawnkeepers the choice will lie between a knapsack sprayer and a low-volume sprayer, the decision depending on the acreage to be treated. To the general horticultural grower or market gardener the low-volume sprayer is, as yet, of little use. If, however, he has an orchard it would be wise to consider the possibility of ground spraying when buying a sprayer for his fruit trees. Otherwise, a knapsack or other small high-volume sprayer will be suitable in the majority of cases.

Points to look for in Spraying Machines.—Having decided on the machine most suited to your needs, there will still be a bewildering array of different makes open to you. It will be worth while, then, to list a few points of detail for consideration.

(*a*) Ease of filling. Filling the machine is a very considerable part of the spraying operation. Much will depend on the farmer's own organization, but considerable time will be saved if the sprayer is easy to fill. Points to note are: 1. Provision of a suction hose. 2. Whether the suction hose will go into a B.O.V. carboy. 3. Size of the filler hole, etc.

(*b*) Provision of a "non-splash" filler hole. When filling a sprayer with acid, D.N.O.C. or D.N.B.P. it can be dangerous if these splash the face or clothes. A non-splash filler hole avoids this.

(*c*) Provision of agitators. Agitators are essential for spraying D.N.O.C., Bordeaux mixture and D.D.T. suspension, and are desirable for some proprietary fungicides. They can also make the mixing of the spray solution very much easier.

(*d*) Provision of an acid-resisting tank. Without this the sprayer cannot be used for B.O.V.

(*e*) Provision of suitable hoses for spraying light oils.

(*f*) Provision of an adequate number of filters, including filters in the nozzles.

(*g*) Provision of a good filter on the suction hose, so that if a pond has to be used as a source of water, small particles of organic matter are not sucked up.

(*h*) Provision of a suitable spray circuit to ensure "non-drip" nozzles.

(*i*) Adaptability. The more jobs for which a sprayer can be used the more economic it will become. Points to note are: 1. Can lances be fitted for spraying underneath potato leaves? 2. Can a hand lance be fitted for spraying trees and clumps of weeds in awkward places? 3. Will the machine work at high pressures for fruit-tree spraying, etc.?

(*j*) The possibility of using one-half of the spray-boom independently of the other and the provision of a safety device in case the boom encounters an obstacle.

(*k*) Cost!

Care of the Spraying Machine.—The first and most important rule in the care of a spraying machine is to obey implicitly the recommendations given in the maker's instruction booklet provided with the machine. In addition it only remains necessary to emphasize one or two points.

1. At the beginning of the spraying season (*a*) thoroughly oil and grease the machine, (*b*) test with clean water and make any repairs, renewals or adjustments necessary.

2. When the machine is in use, (*a*) use clean water for making up spray solutions, (*b*) rinse the machine out with clean water at the end of each day's work, (*c*) examine filters regularly, preferably after each day's work, (*d*) keep well greased and oiled.

3. After the season's work (*a*) thoroughly wash out the machinery with several changes of clean water, using warm soapy water for the first washing; (*b*) where machines have been used for acid, wash first with a dilute solution of washing soda; (*c*) remove all rubber connections and hoses, wash thoroughly and store in a cool, dry room; (*d*) remove all chains and store in oil; (*e*) wash down the outside of the machine and repaint where necessary; (*f*) store under cover and if the machine has rubber-tyred wheels set it up on blocks so that the tyres are clear of the ground; (*g*) grease boom and nozzles to prevent corrosion.

Using the Sprayer.—Finally, when using the sprayer observe one or two rules which, though easy to write, are harder to practise:

1. Make sure you cover all the ground. Nothing looks worse than thin strips of weeds left across fields, where

spraying has not joined. On the other hand, try not to overlap too much as you might damage the crop by putting on twice as much weedkiller as is necessary. When working in large fields it is often a good practice to have a second man—even if the tractor and sprayer is a one-man outfit—to move markers to ensure a good join-up of successive belts of spraying, to speed up refilling and to watch for blocked-up nozzles.

2. Avoid catching the spray boom on hedges, gate-posts and trees, etc.

3. Don't spray when the wind is likely to carry the weedkiller on to susceptible crops (even if they are not your own!).

4. Observe ALL the precautions given in Chapters Nine and Ten, particularly for B.O.V., D.N.O.C., D.N.B.P.— your life may depend on it!

CHAPTER FIFTEEN

SPECIAL METHODS FOR SPECIAL WEEDS

So FAR we have dealt with the control of weeds generally, but there are a number of weeds which, because of the difficulty of controlling them, require a more specific treatment. These weeds and their control are the subject of this and the following chapter.

COUCH (*Agropyron repens*)

Couch is a grass closely related to the cultivated wheats and, indeed, at one time bore the generic name of the wheats (i.e. *Triticum*). The same name "Couch" is also used for some other weed grasses including the Bents (*Agrostis spp.*) and Onion Couch (*Arrhenatherum tuberosum*), but in this section we are concerned mainly with *Agropyron repens*.

The main reason why Couch is such a tenacious weed and so difficult to control is because it has a strong system of underground stems (rhizomes). Root systems form from the nodes of these stems and buds grow up to form new plants. Shoots from the rhizomes can begin to grow as early as February, and during the Spring and Summer a strong, tall-growing, flowering stem is produced. The plant thus propagates itself in two ways, by seed and by its underground stems. Spread by the latter method is often considerably assisted by cultivations which break up the rhizome scattering the pieces, each of which will produce a new plant. Although the spread by means of underground stems is probably the more important, that due to seed is not to be overlooked and everything possible should be done to prevent hedgerow infestations becoming a source of infection for crops.

The method employed to eradicate Couch will depend on the type of soil. The problem is most difficult in heavy soils, under which conditions the effective methods include bare fallowing, bastard fallowing, the Scarlett method, and the use of sodium chlorate applied at 2–3 cwt. per acre in the Autumn. In lighter soils the best method of approach is to get the weed, including the rhizomes, on the surface of the soil for collecting and burning. A good method of achieving this is to plough in early Spring at a depth which is sufficient to under-cut the rhizomes and then, during dry spells, to cultivate the ground with a wheeled-type cultivator or drag harrow to bring the rhizomes to the surface. This operation should not be carried out in wet periods. Once on the surface, rhizomes should be freed of soil, again while the weather is dry, by rolling; collected into heaps by means of a chain harrow or rake and burnt. Dry weather is essential for the success of this method; if wet, instead of pulverizing and freeing the rhizomes, the soil will break up into little clods containing pieces of underground stem and the spread of the weed will be encouraged. The same method can also be employed very successfully against Onion Couch, although for this weed frequent ploughings when the soil is dry is probably the best method.

An old method of controlling Couch is suggested by its generic name "*Agropyron*", which means "field fire". Small fires were lit all over the infested field so that the field itself appeared to be on fire. In heavy-land districts this method also had the effect of improving the soil texture.

As yet no control of Couch by selective weedkillers is practicable but a new chemical, called T.C.A., does offer promise in this respect (*see* Chapter Nine).

DODDER AND BROOMRAPES (*Cuscuta spp.* and *Orobanche spp.*)

Dodders and Broomrapes are often thought of together because both are parasitic weeds (*see* Chapter One) and both attack clover, but there the similarity ends, for botanically they are quite different plants bearing no resemblance to each other in appearance, habit of growth, or in the way they are controlled. We shall, therefore, consider them separately. Neither plant is very common at the present time; the only reason for devoting so much space to them here is their considerable interest value.

There are many species of Dodder which attack many

different plants, but in this country the most important one is mainly a parasite of red clover and lucerne called *Cuscuta trifolii*. It is possible, however, there are several strains of this species; the strains which attack clover may not be able to attack lucerne and vice versa. The seeds of Dodder are round, about 1 mm. in diameter and brown in colour. They were very frequently found in clover and lucerne seed samples, but this tendency has greatly decreased in more recent years; under the *Seeds Regulations* 1922 (*see* Chapter Two) the amount of Dodder present in seeds offered for sale is very rigidly controlled.

Dodder is an annual plant; that is to say it grows afresh from seed each year and does not live from year to year in the vegetative state. Under favourable conditions the seed germinates very rapidly, producing a short root and a long thread-like stem. As it grows the stem rotates in a wide circle in the hope of making contact with a suitable host plant. Failing to make contact, it dies, but succeeding, it twines itself round the host plant and puts out little suckers ("haustoria") into the stems. Once established it derives all its nutriment from the host and becomes severed from its root. When mature the plant is a mass of reddish-brown, leafless threads twining themselves amongst the clover or lucerne stems and bearing clusters of small white, bell-shaped flowers. Each flower produces four seeds which are either shed to reinfest the ground or are harvested with the seed of the host plant. If the stems of the plant become broken, each section starts life on its own to produce a new plant. Because of the continual removal of food by the Dodder the clover plant dies, the net effect being to give dead patches of clover throughout the crop wherever the weed is present.

Control of Dodder is fairly easy, but involves losing the clover, although, as it would probably be killed anyway, this is no great disadvantage. It is far better, however, to prevent the weed getting into the crop by having samples of red clover and lucerne seed tested for purity at the appropriate Seed Testing Station (*see* Appendix I).

Where patches of Dodder occur in a crop they can be controlled in one of two ways:

1. They can be covered with a layer of straw or chaff about 6–8 inches thick, sprinkled with paraffin and burnt. By this treatment both Dodder and clover are completely destroyed without moving them. It should be carried out before the Dodder produces seed, otherwise an infection will be left in the ground.

2. They can be sprayed with a solution of sulphuric acid, containing 13 gallons of B.O.V. per 80 gallons of spray. This treatment, too, will destroy both parasite and host.

On no account should any attempt be made to rake out Dodder, as this will only break up the stems and spread the weed. Where a field has been infested with Dodder it should be rested from leguminous crops for a number of years. Dodder seed is capable of passing through cattle unharmed.

The species of Broomrape usually found in Britain is the Lesser Broomrape (*Orobanche minor*). It is more common than Dodder but is of less importance as, even in severe infestations, the damage done appears to be slight. It will attack most species of clover.

The seeds of Broomrape are very tiny and produced in very large numbers, probably between 50,000 and 100,000 per plant. The seed germinates when it comes into contact with the root of a suitable host and produces a threadlike seedling which becomes attached to the roots of the host plant by means of suckers. Once established the plant produces a succulent, scaly, flowering stem, about $\frac{1}{4}$ inch thick, bearing a spike of reddish, trumpet-shaped flowers. The seeds are shed before the clover is harvested for seed, making it rare to find Broomrape in the seed sample. Once in the soil the seeds may remain dormant for several years.

The usually recommended ways of combating Broomrape are hand pulling and rotation using lucerne and sainfoin to take the place of clover.

GROUND ELDER (*Aegopodium podagraria*)

Ground Elder might well be described as one of the unsolved weed problems of the garden. The trouble is not so much that no means of control have ever been evolved but a treatment which works well for one person never seems to work for anyone else. This makes the task of the adviser rather an exasperating one. In this section I shall describe methods of control which have worked with some people but give no guarantee they will work with you. First, however, let us say a little about the weed itself. Ground Elder is a member of the family called the *Umbelliferae*, which includes many common weeds of field and hedgerow, such as Rough Chervil (*Chaerophyllum temulum*), Fool's Parsley (*Aethusa cynapiun*), Shepherd's Needle (*Scandix pecten-veneris*), Earthnut (*Conopodium majus*), and Caraway (*Carum carvi*). Its persistence is due mainly to the fact that it produces very brittle rhizomes, and cultivations only tend to break the rhizomes and spread the weed. The methods of control aim at stopping the weed from producing foliage, thereby starving the rhizomes, which eventually die.

The control methods suggested are:

1. Continuous pulling or hoeing of the young shoots. Admittedly this is a soul-destroying job, but if sufficiently repeated, can bring success.

2. Repeated digging of the ground, producing, on a garden scale, conditions something like a bare fallow.

3. Complete digging out of the plant and rhizomes. This is only possible while the weed is confined to small patches.

4. Treatment with sodium chlorate at the rate of 1 oz. per square yard. Such treatment will, of course, make the soil useless for some considerable time and cannot be used where the weed is among bushes or fruit trees. Ground Elder can, however, be amazingly resistant to sodium chlorate.

HOARY PEPPERWORT (*Cardaria draba*)

Hoary Pepperwort is a weed belonging to the family "Cruciferae" and is found on all types of soil, mainly in eastern and southern England. Infestations usually start as a small patch, probably originating from a seed, but soon spread and are exceedingly difficult to control. The reason for this is that the plant has a strong creeping-root system which will not only penetrate the soil to a considerable depth, but will also grow horizontally for distances of 30 or more feet. Once established in a field, there seems little doubt the chief means of spread is by these roots rather than by seed.

In the past many different methods have been tried to eradicate Hoary Pepperwort but with little success. An answer to the problem has recently been provided, however, with the use of M.C.P.A. and 2,4-D. Both these materials are effective against the weed, provided treatment is continued for two or three consecutive years. On heavy soils it is recommended that treatment should be made in two consecutive Autumn-sown cereal crops and, if necessary, a third Spring-sown crop which is resistant to either M.C.P.A. or 2,4-D. On light and medium soils where Spring cropping is an easier proposition, application of the weedkillers should be made to two or three consecutive Spring cereal crops. By spraying Spring-sown crops the damage done to the weed by the Spring cultivation is added to that achieved by the weedkiller. Whichever growth regulator is used, it should be applied as a spray at the rate of 2 lb. of the acid equivalent per acre.

An interesting fact which has arisen out of Blackman and Holly's experiments on the control of Hoary Pepperwort* is that the best time for application of the weedkiller varies with M.C.P.A. and 2,4-D. The former gives its greatest effect when applied in the flower-bud stage and the latter when the weed is in full flower. This was one of the first indications that time of application could be a very critical factor in the use of the growth regulators.

RUSHES (*Juncus spp.*)

In some parts of the country Rushes are a common weed of pasture land. The main species concerned is *Juncus effusus*, although *J. conglomeratus* and *J. inflexus* may also occur.

Rushes have, for a long time, been considered an indication that the land needed draining, but this is not always the

* *Agriculture* (1949), 56; 1; 6–11. G. E. Blackman and K. Holly.

case. Recent investigations have shown that the presence of Rushes is much more an indication of impoverished soil.*

The control of Rushes must be considered in two parts; firstly the eradication of those already established in the pasture and secondly the prevention of reinfestation.

Rushes can be eradicated by ploughing up and reseeding, although some degree of control can also be achieved by mowing during July or August. The Common Rush, *Juncus effusus*, can also be controlled by means of M.C.P.A. or 2,4-D, the latter being slightly the more effective. Application should be made at a rate of 2 lb. acid-equivalent per acre during June. The cutting of the Rushes either a month before or a month after spraying increases the effectiveness of the treatment. Whether reseeding, cutting or spraying is adopted, it is essential that the impoverished condition of the soil should be corrected at the same time. Draining and liming should be carried out where necessary, and the nitrogen, phosphate and potash status of the soil restored. Where land is reseeded it should be grazed for the first year.

The Rush plant produces phenomenal amounts of seed. It has been calculated that a single panicle will produce over 8,000 seeds and in a reasonably infested pasture over 8,000,000 seeds can be produced per square yard in a season. Added to this the seed is able to remain viable in the soil for about sixty years. Thus it will be seen that where Rushes have infested a field, even when the Rushes themselves have been eradicated, there is still ample chance for reinfestation. Fortunately, the Rush seedling is very susceptible to competition and no matter how many seeds are in the soil, provided a vigorous competitive sward is built up and maintained, the Rush seedlings will have little chance of survival. Having cleared a pasture of Rushes, then, the way to keep it clear is by GOOD GRASSLAND MANAGEMENT (*see* Chapter Three).

WILD OATS (*Avena fatua* and *Avena ludoviciana*)

The Wild Oat is a serious weed of cereal crops; serious because not only has its prevalence greatly increased during

* *J. Board Greenkeeping Res.* (1950), 7; 26; 356–61. H. I. Moore.

the last ten years, but also, at the moment, it is almost impossible to control it with any certainty.

The reasons for its success as a weed are as follows:

1. Being a very close relative of the cereals, conditions of cultivation which favour these crops also favour the weed, and the selective weedkillers used in corn are of no effect.

2. The Wild Oat sheds its seed before the cereal crop in which it is growing is harvested.

3. When present in oats, seeds which are harvested with the crop are impossible to remove by mechanical cleaning, and even seeds which are harvested while they are quite immature are able to germinate normally.

4. The seeds exhibit dormancy which can be of three kinds (*see* Chapter Two). Firstly, after the seed has been shed it may require a normal resting period (i.e. natural dormancy) of about four months before it germinates. Secondly, if conditions are not suitable for its growth, it enters a period of induced dormancy which may last three years or perhaps more. Thirdly, Russian work has shown that where seeds, after they have been shed, are subjected to alternate wetting and drying they exhibit a form of dormancy called "secondary dormancy".* We still, how-ever, have much to learn about the dormancy of Wild Oats.

5. Seeds lying on the surface of the ground are able to bury themselves by the action of their awns, which stretch out and contract during alternating spells of wet and dry weather. Once buried the seeds cease to be susceptible to the scavenging activities of wild birds.

On the question of controlling Wild Oats, the best one can do is to make suggestions which are worth trying. Obviously the more suggestions which can be practised at any one time, the greater the chances of success. Possible methods of attack, then, are:

---

* *Agriculture* (1948), 55; 1; 13. W. E. Brenchley and J. M. Thurston.

1. Autumn cleaning (*see* Chapter Four). Stubble cleaning is of little avail because of the natural dormancy of the seed. Neither are bare fallows completely effective against Wild Oats. Autumn cleaning, however, if continued till after Christmas, extends beyond the period of natural dormancy and kills the first crop of seedlings.

2. Introducing a ley of over three years' duration. The seeds of Wild Oats are not very long lived and under the conditions of a long ley most of them will probably die and the chances of new seed being produced are small.

3. Two successive years of late-planted cleaning crops e.g. brussels, cabbage, rape or kale, followed by a Winter cereal. The seedlings formed from seeds germinating during the period of the cleaning crops will be killed by the pre-sowing and inter-row cultivations and, as Winter cereals are the first to be harvested, there is a good chance of plants growing from seeds remaining in the third year being cut before their seed is shed.

4. Running a large flock of hens over the stubble. The hens will not only eat those seeds lying on the surface, but tend to scratch up those which have become buried. It has been suggested that this treatment is improved if the hens are left unfed!

5. It will have been noticed in preceding chapters, that oats are susceptible to D.N.B.P. This has suggested that D.N.B.P. might possibly be used for controlling Wild Oats in peas. Farmers who have tried the treatment have had varying degrees of success, but 100% kills of Oats have been claimed.* The difficulty is, however, that all the conditions for success—weeds in the seedling stage, crop at the six-leaf stage, air temperature above 55°, and the weather dry—rarely occur at the same time. Nevertheless, when the conditions are right, the method is worth a trial, if only on a small area.

While the control of Wild Oats is very difficult, there are two effective means of prevention. The first is CLEAN SEED, the second A GOOD ROTATION. As has already

* *The Farmers' Weekly*, July 18th, 1952, p. 29. S. G. Wise.

been remarked earlier, it is impossible to remove Wild Oats from ordinary oats by mechanical methods, but it is possible to avoid taking seed from crops which contain the weed. To take seed from such crops is to invite trouble and should be avoided at all costs. Much of the present increase in Wild Oats is undoubtedly due to the practice of taking several white straw crops in successive years. Where a good rotation is practised, including cleaning crops and leys, the possibility of a build-up of Wild Oats will be reduced to a minimum.

WILD ONION (*Alliun vineale*)

Wild Onion, while it will grow on several soil types, is mainly a weed of heavy land and seems to be very localized in its occurrence. Although it is an unpleasant weed and difficult to control, as a plant it is very interesting because of its varied means of propagation. Also, its control is a good example of theory and practice going hand in hand, as it was not until the life cycle of the weed was understood that a satisfactory means of eradication could be developed. The importance of Wild Onion as a weed lies in the fact that the bulbils will taint corn to such an extent as to make it unmillable or even unthreshable, and if eaten by stock it will taint their milk.

The weed can be propagated in four ways: by soft bulbs, hard bulbs, bulbils and seeds. From the practical point of view the seeds are of no importance; it is the three vegetative means of propagation which are responsible for the weed being such a pest. The plant begins to grow rapidly in the early Autumn and looks very much like an ordinary onion. In the early Spring, hard bulbs are formed on the outside of the parent soft bulb and the flowering stem begins to develop. By early Summer the flowering stem is fully developed and produces a mass of "bulbils" at its head. The bulbils are greenish-white in colour, fleshy, rather like a fig in shape and about the size of a wheat grain. Those bulbils which are not harvested with the grain are scattered on the ground and may either begin to grow the following late Autumn or early Spring, or remain dormant for a year or two. The clusters of hard bulbs around the soft bulbs become broken up by cultivation and these also produce new plants.

K

A successful method for controlling Wild Onion has been developed by Mr. J. R. Tinney, an Essex farmer. The paper describing his method was published in the *Journal of the Ministry of Agriculture* ("Agriculture", Volume 49) in December 1942, and has been quoted so often that it must now surely be considered a classic. I make no apology, therefore, for quoting in full the method of eradication propounded by Mr. Tinney in his paper:

The writer's recommendations for the complete eradication of Wild Onions comprised a specific rotation, such as that detailed below. This must be adhered to religiously, and it is of particular importance that plough-ing should be done at the time stated. The writer is also of the opinion that six years' spring corn is not sufficiently drastic to effect a hundred per cent. clearance, and any-thing short of this is of little use.

1*st* *Year*. POTATOES or SUGAR BEET. Plough as deeply as possible during the previous November (not earlier). Otherwise good farming methods for a clean crop and maximum yield.

2*nd* *Year*. SPRING WHEAT or BARLEY. Plough in previous November (not earlier). Otherwise normal cultivations.

3*rd* *Year*. SUGAR BEET or POTATOES. Plough in previous November (not earlier). Otherwise normal cultivations.

4*th* *Year*. BARLEY or SPRING WHEAT or SPRING OATS. Plough in previous November (not earlier).

5*th* *Year*. Any SPRING GREEN CROP such as peas, kale, cabbage, silage, etc. Plough in previous November (not earlier).

6*th* *Year*. SPRING CORN. Plough in previous November (not earlier).

It is essential that the first crop in the rotation should be potatoes or roots, and that there should be two cleaning crops in the first three years of the rotation. It is pointed out also that a succession of six spring-sown corn crops would fail entirely to get rid of the onions.

The essential features of this scheme of cropping are, therefore: (1) a succession of spring-sown crops for a minimum period of six years; and (2) the omission of such crops as autumn-sown wheat, beans, clover and bare fallow. These and other matters of importance may be condensed into seven golden rules, which must be observed for a period of not less than six years.

(1) NEVER "PULL" THE ONIONS.

An attempt to eliminate wild Onions by "pulling" the plants cannot succeed, since for each one pulled a "litter" of hard bulbs may be left in the ground.

(2) NEVER INTRODUCE A BARE FALLOW.

A bare fallow does not kill onions, it only distributes them.

(3) NEVER PLOUGH IN SEPTEMBER OR OCTOBER.

Ploughing in September (or October) offers the onions ideal conditions for rapid Autumn growth culminating in the formation of hard bulbs before Spring cultivations commence. On the other hand, if ploughing is delayed until November, the life-cycle of the onion plant is cut in two: vigorous autumn growth is destroyed and the interval before spring cultivations is too short to permit full development. A severe check is given to the plants when they are most vulnerable, and the formation of resistant bulbs is inhibited.

(4) NEVER SOW WINTER CEREALS OR WINTER BEANS.

The conditions which are ideal for winter wheat and beans are also ideal for the triple propagation of Wild Onions. When these crops are harvested there will be aerial bulblets in profusion, as well as batteries of underground bulbs. Obviously such crops cannot find a place in the six years' programme of eradication. Whatever the sacrifice they must be excluded.

(5) NEVER SOW CLOVER OR SEED MIXTURES
for short or long leys, or sainfoin or lucerne alone or in
mixtures.

A clover ley or any longer ley with seeds mixtures or
lucerne prevents the formation of aerial bulblets (if the
hay is cut in June) but, underground, the bulbs can
multiply. Even in a ley of several years' duration the
weed will multiply.

(6) NEVER ATTEMPT TO ELIMINATE WILD
ONIONS ON WET LAND UNTIL IT IS
DRAINED.

There is no need to emphasize the need for drainage
on heavy land. So far as Wild Onions are concerned,
it would be futile to attempt their eradication unless
the field had been mole-drained during the past five
or six years.

(7) NEVER ASSUME THE ABSENCE OF WILD
ONIONS, even if they cannot be seen, until the six
years' programme has been completed. Spring cropping and late ploughing prevent the formation of aerial
bulblets or so-called "seed", and also check the
formation of hard bulbs in the soil, so that propagation
is suspended. The continued existence of the weed
therefore depends on the survival rate of hard bulbs
lying dormant in the soil.

CHAPTER SIXTEEN

SOME CRYPTOGAMS AND THEIR CONTROL

SO FAR we have dealt mainly with weeds which belong to the large group of the plant kingdom sometimes called the Phanerogams (plants with visible flowers), and sometimes the Spermaphyta (i.e. seed-bearing plants). Those plants which do not bear seeds in the true sense are put into another group called the Cryptogams (plants with hidden "flowers"). In these plants the reproductive unit equivalent to the seed is called a "spore". The spores are produced in or on various types of organ but these bear no resemblance to the typical flower of the Phanerogams.

The Cryptogams can be subdivided into three further groups, namely the Pteridophyta (the fern plants), the Bryophyta (the moss-like plants) and the Thallophyta (plants consisting of threads). Each of these sub-groups contain plants which must be considered as important weeds. Among the Pteridophyta are Bracken (*Pteris aquilinum*), and the Horse-tails (*Equisetum spp.*), among the Bryophyta the Mosses, and among the Thallophyta the Toadstools which cause Fairy Rings.

BRACKEN (*Pteris aquilinum*)

Bracken is a member of the group of plants we call ferns and is a serious weed of hill and moorland pasture. The plant consists of a mass of underground stems (rhizomes), which infest the soil at various levels to a depth of about 2 feet. The stems near the surface of the ground produce buds from which the typical fern-like leaves (fronds) of the Bracken arise. It was thought at one time that there was an interval of several years between the formation of the bud on the rhizome and the formation of the frond, but it has now been shown* that the fronds can be produced in a few weeks. This rapid rate of

* *Nature* (1943), 152, 751. K. W. Braid and E. Conway.

growth is one of the factors which make Bracken so difficult to control; another factor is the large quantities of food stored in the rhizomes. It is known* that where the growth of Bracken is strong and dense there may be as much as 40 tons per acre of rhizome beneath the soil. The food stored in the rhizomes is produced in the fronds by photosynthesis.

Undoubtedly, the best means of controlling Bracken, where possible, is to plough and put the ground through an arable rotation before reseeding, although direct reseeding is also possible. A good crop with which to begin an arable rotation is potatoes. On many hill pastures, however, where Bracken is usually found, ploughing is often either unpracticable or uneconomic. In such cases other methods of control have to be practised. In nearly all these the aim is to exhaust the rhizome of food. This is achieved by continually destroying the fronds so that not only is no new food produced but the food already in the rhizome is used up in the production of new buds. A number of methods of destroying the fronds have been tried; these are cutting, bruising, treading and chemical treatment.

Cutting appears to be the most successful method to date. The most satisfactory tool for this job is the scythe, but, except for small patches, hand labour is too expensive. Usually the operation is either carried out with an ordinary type of reciprocating-blade mower or with a special machine with a revolving arm which slashes off the Bracken fronds. The Bracken should be cut at least twice a year and the treatment continued for two years or more. The best time for the first cut is between the beginning of June and the middle of July. The second cut should be made as soon as the fronds are sufficiently high to make the operation practicable.

Mowers, however, have the disadvantage that where the ground is very uneven or where rocks and boulders project above the surface, the cutter bar is easily damaged. To overcome this objection, special machines have been developed for the purpose of crushing the Bracken fronds without their being actually severed from the plant. These machines can

* *Agriculture* (1940), 47; 1; 55–62. W. G. R. Paterson.

cover the ground fairly quickly and are not greatly impeded by low rocks or uneven ground. Bruising, however, is not so efficient as cutting and must be continued for three or four years or even longer to control the Bracken effectively. Other disadvantages of the bruising method are, firstly, the fronds are not killed quickly and are able to continue photosynthesis for some considerable time, and secondly, the fronds do not wither as do the cut ones, but form a thick covering to the ground through which the grass finds it difficult to penetrate to compete effectively with the Bracken. Bruising should be carried out at least twice a year, at the same times as recommended for cutting.

Treading with sheep, hens, pigs and cows while the fronds are young has also been suggested as a possible remedy for Bracken. The treading must be very concentrated to be really effective, and often the question of economics, which is of major importance in Bracken control, rears its ugly head. Another difficulty here is that Bracken is poisonous. Usually the plant is not eaten by stock, but it has been suggested* that where grass is very rich animals may turn to it as a source of fibre. Such a tendency could be avoided by having hay or straw available.

Bracken can be controlled by the use of sodium chlorate at 2–3 cwt. per acre and the fronds can be destroyed with B.O.V., but both these treatments are too dear to be of practical usefulness. Sodium chlorate, however, may be used to kill small pockets of the weed which are missed by the mower or bruising machine, though, of course, the grass will also be killed.

Bracken is not an entirely useless material, it can be used to make a rather unpalatable silage,† as bedding, for compost, as a covering material for potato clamps and as a thatch for animal shelters.

HORSETAILS (*Equisetum spp.*)

The Horsetail plant consists of a strong creeping root-stock from which are produced sterile, upright, hollow, jointed

---

* *Agriculture* (1949), 56; 5; 204–5. H. E. Wells.
† *J. Agric. Sc.* (1944), 34; 3; 172–5. W. S. Ferguson and O. Heave.

stems of a greenish-white colour. At each joint the stem
carries a whorl of jointed branches, but there are no leaves in
the true sense. During April and May special non-branching
stems are produced, looking rather like asparagus shoots, at
the apices of which the spores are produced. These fertile
shoots soon die, but the sterile ones remain all the Summer.
The two species mainly encountered in this country are
Equisetum palustre and *Equisetum arvense*.

The chief importance of Horsetails lies in the fact that they
are poisonous to stock and retain this property in hay. Thus,
although they are found in both arable and pasture land, they
are a particular nuisance in the latter. When Horsetails are
eaten they cause animals to scour, lose condition, and, in the
case of dairy cows, a rapid drop in their milk yield. This effect
is caused by a special enzyme contained within the plant and
not so much by their coarse nature as was once supposed.
Cattle do not usually eat the plants, but may do so if grass is
scarce or so thick that discrimination by the animal is
impossible.

Until recently the control recommended for Horsetail was
GOOD HUSBANDRY and this must still play an important
part, but in 1952 a method using M.C.P.A. was suggested
by Dr. William Plant.* For effective control of Horsetail in
pasture, Dr. Plant recommends using M.C.P.A. at the rate of
1 lb. acid equivalent per acre as a low-volume spray at 5–15
gallons per acre. It is interesting to note that he has found
that to use more than 1 lb. per acre decreases the effectiveness
of the weedkiller; thus where other weeds have to be sprayed
as well with higher rates, these should be treated first and the
Horsetail treatment followed 6–8 weeks later. The best time
for treatment is when the maximum number of Horsetail
shoots are present and the weed is sufficiently clear of grass to
be completely covered with the spray. This can be any time
between May and September, but late May is probably the
most convenient. Having controlled the Horsetails in this way
it is essential to follow up with GOOD GRASSLAND
MANAGEMENT. Work by other experimenters, however,
suggests that usually the control of Horsetails achieved by

* *Agriculture* (1952), 59; 2; 86–8. W. Plant.

using either M.C.P.A. or 2,4-D is only of a temporary nature and that the weed grows again subsequently.

Moss in Lawns

One of the worst curses of the lawn is Moss. The growth of the plant, of which there are many species, takes place in two stages. The spore first germinates to produce a network of fine, thread-like growths almost invisible to the naked eye, called the protonema. Then, from the protonema, develop the typical fronds of the Moss and root-like structures called rhizoids. During the Spring and Autumn a cup-like structure is produced from the fronds on a little stalk, and in this the new spores are formed. Apart from reproducing by spores, if the shoots or rhizoids of the Moss become broken up, e.g. during raking, then each section is capable of producing a protonema and hence a new plant.

Moss is a nuisance because not only does it leave unsightly bare patches in the lawn during the Summer, but also makes the turf slippery.

A number of recommendations have been made in the past for its control, of which two are given here:

(a) Lawn sand. A suitable mixture is 3 parts sulphate of ammonia, 1 part calcined sulphate of iron and 15 parts sand applied at a rate of 4–6 oz. per square yard, several times during the Spring and Summer.

(b) Treatment with a solution of sulphate of iron containing 1 oz. per gallon and applied at a rate of 1 gallon per square yard.

While these treatments may destroy the current growth of Moss, they do not, however, kill the spores which remain in the soil to produce a further infestation in a subsequent season. It has been claimed recently* that Moss, including its spores, can be controlled by the use of certain non-poisonous compounds of mercury. These are now on the market either incorporated in a lawn sand or as a straight chemical treat-

* *Gardener's Chronicle*, Dec. 13th, 1952. I. Greenfield.

ment. Whatever chemical treatment is used it must be followed up by good lawn management.

FAIRY RINGS

Fairy Rings are caused by fungi which are present in the soil as a mass (*mycelium*) of fine, white threads (*hyphae*). These fungi, of which there are many different kinds, reveal their presence by their fruiting bodies, which may be either toadstools or puffballs. In the case of the toadstools, the spores are formed on the gills underneath the "umbrella" part (*pileus*), and in the case of the puffballs they are formed within the ball.

A Fairy Ring starts as a spot, but as the fungus grows out from the spot the older mycelium in the centre dies away leaving a ring of actively growing fungus. As the fungus continues to grow so the ring gets bigger. The ring can be seen because the young fungus on the outside stimulates the grass, giving it that very green appearance, but as the fungus gets older it kills the grass. It does this in two ways: by poisoning the grass and by making a layer just below the soil surface which rain cannot penetrate, causing the grass to die through lack of water. The structure of a Fairy Ring is shown in Fig. 13.

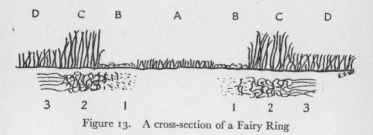

Figure 13.   A cross-section of a Fairy Ring

KEY TO FIGURE 13

A—grass recovering.   1.—old fungus.
B—dead grass.   2.—mature fungus.
C—stimulated grass   3.—young fungus.
D—normal grass.

There is only one certain way of controlling Fairy Rings;*
that is by digging out the infected turf and soil and by steriliz-
ing the sub-soil. The best time to do this is in the Autumn.
The soil should be removed to a depth of 9 inches and the
operation should extend to at least a foot outside the ring to be
sure of removing all the fungus (*see* Fig. 13). The excavated
area should then be soaked with a solution of formaldehyde,
containing ½ pint per 25 gallons of water, and left over-
night covered with a tarpaulin; the formaldehyde must be
kept off the grass or it will kill it. After the treatment the area
should be filled with fresh clean soil and returfed.

Another chemical method suggested for controlling Fairy
Rings consists of watering the grass with a solution of iron
sulphate, containing ½ oz. per gallon of water, at the rate of
1 gallon per square yard.

The success of this method, however, depends on the
species of fungi present.

Fairy Rings can be kept in check by watering outside the
ring with a solution of corrosive sublimate containing 1 oz. per
5 gallons of water. The ground should first be thoroughly
prodded with a fork and then a good soaking given with the
corrosive sublimate solution, followed by an equal quantity of
water. Corrosive sublimate is very poisonous and great care
should be taken in using it. It should be locked away from
animals and children.

* *J. Board of Greenkeeping Res.* (1949), 7; 25; 274–5.

CHAPTER SEVENTEEN

PAST, PRESENT AND FUTURE

THE practice of selective weed control began in the late nineteenth century with Bonnet's demonstration of the use of copper sulphate to kill Charlock in cereals. Although following this there was a haphazard trial of other chemicals, it was not until 1911, with the publication of Rabate's work on the use of sulphuric acid, that another real step forward was made. Like Gray's ploughman the practice then plodded its weary way through another twenty years until 1933 saw the development, again in France, of D.N.O.C. In 1940, three workers (Slade, Templeman and Sexton), at the Jealott's Hill Research Station of Imperial Chemical Industries, made a new and fascinating discovery which resulted, in 1942, in the introduction as a weedkiller of the growth regulator we now call M.C.P.A.* But in 1939, three years before this development was complete, came World War II.

There is a saying "It's an ill wind that blows nobody any good", and without in any way wishing to minimize the tragedy of the war, it must be admitted it did a great deal of good for the practice of selective weedkilling. With the shortage of food and the need for getting the last ounce from our arable land, effective weed control was essential. Under the leadership of Prof. Blackman a team of workers set about the task of examining the possibilities of the weedkillers available, and their results, together with those of other workers who had taken up the challenge, began to appear in 1944. By 1946, the golden jubilee of Bonnet's work, Prof. Blackman was able to write "it is true to say that more has been learned about selective weed control in England during the last five years than in the whole of the previous forty-five".† To this period must largely be ascribed the development of the use in

---

* For a full history of the discovery of M.C.P.A. and 2,4-D see *Plant Growth Substances*. L. J. Audus. (Leonard Hill Ltd.)

† *Jour. of Min. of Agric.* (1946), 53; 1; 16. G. E. Blackman.

Britain of copper chloride, D.N.O.C. and M.C.P.A. as selective weedkillers. A certain amount of investigation was also carried out in the use of D.C.P.A., but the Americans took a more fanatical interest in this material and were largely responsible for its development. In America it was known by the configuration "2,4-D" and this seems to have "stuck" in preference to the British "D.C.P.A.". Without seeming unpatriotic may I say the American term has the advantage of being less easily confused with M.C.P.A., particularly in speech. The period since the war has largely been a time of consolidation of wartime advances in knowledge, although a number of new weedkillers have appeared including the light oils, D.N.B.P. and 2,4,5,-T. Another big advance during the last few years, however, which must not be overlooked, has been the development of the low-volume sprayer. This was, and is, a tool which even some of the smaller farmers could afford and has done much in taking the weedkillers to the farms.

THE PRESENT

Today the farmer, the horticulturist and the gardener have at their disposal a wide range of selective weedkillers with almost as wide a range of usefulness. The farmer can control many of his corn and grassland weeds in the ease of his tractor seat, the horticulturist can destroy the invaders of his onion, leek and carrot beds and the gardener has at hand the easiest means he has ever had of keeping his lawn clean and tidy.

Colourful advertisements proclaim the wonders of substances which only a few years ago were chemical oddities while "hormone weedkillers" (however much the scientist may dislike the term) are discussed in the village inn.

But this is only one side of the story. Rapid advances such as we have seen in selective weed control have their drawbacks. Let it be quite clear, it is the *practice* of selective weed control that has made the advance and inevitably the *science* (the why and wherefore) has been left behind. We know *what* selective weedkillers do, but very much less about *how* they do it. Some may think the acquisition of basic knowledge (sometimes miscalled "theory") is unnecessary, but it is the foundation of sound practice. To build without a foundation is to invite a fall! While the present position of selective weed control is praiseworthy, a good deal more research still needs to be done on such problems as the mode of action of selective weedkillers, the mechanism of plant resistance and susceptibility, the varying effect with different times of application, the effect on the soil fauna, the possibility of unconsciously selecting resistant varieties of those species at present considered susceptible and the long-term effects of drastic changes in the weed flora. These and others are the problems which face us, and until we begin to solve them the whole practice of selective weed control will remain empirical, being dependent ŏn experience gained by a process of trial and error.

THE FUTURE

What of the future? Two lines of development are possible, an extension of the usefulness of present known weedkillers and the discovery of new ones.

Some possible new uses for our present range of selective weedkillers have already been mentioned, for example the use of M.C.P.A. on asparagus, of light oils in forestry nurseries, and of 2,4-D and D.N.B.P. in strawberries. There are a number of others, such as the use of chemicals against weeds in waterways and the use of 2,4-D and D.N.B.P. as pre-emergence treatments, but on the whole the scope in this field would seem to be limited particularly until more is known of the science of the selective action of herbicides. The possibility of new chemicals for new jobs seems a more advantageous, if bewildering, approach, but although new materials are being tested almost daily, only a few at the moment show any promise. Perhaps of all ideas in recent years the most novel has been the investigation of electrical methods of weed control and of these we may well hear more.

With all our aspirations for the future, however, we must keep an eye on the past. It would be a retrograde step if, in the rush of new developments, the old and well-tried methods of good husbandry were forgotten. We must keep in mind that ALL weedkillers, despite their great usefulness, are an extra item on the debit side of the accounts and that, where equally good results can be obtained by sound cultural practice, costs of production will be lower and profits higher. In other words, returning to the premises with which we began this book, any method of weed control will stand or fall in the eyes of the commercial grower not because it is new or novel, or even because it is old-fashioned, but because it pays.

ACKNOWLEDGMENTS

THE author acknowledges the assistance afforded him by: The Controller of Her Majesty's Stationery Office in granting permission to reproduce a considerable section of an article in *Agriculture*, the Journal of the Ministry of Agriculture, entitled "Wild Onions", by Mr. J. R. Tinney (49, 3); and the following for their permission to reproduce photographs and line drawings indicated in brackets.

The Controller of Her Majesty's Stationery Office (Figures 8, 11, 12, from Ministry of Agriculture and Fisheries National Agricultural Advisory Service Farm Machinery Leaflet, No. 14, entitled "Field Crop Sprayers").

The Director of the Sports Turf Research Institute (Plate 4b).

Four Oaks Spraying Machine Co. Ltd. (Plates 6b and 6c).

H. W. Gardner (Plates 1a, 3a and 4a).

Imperial Chemical Industries (Plates 2a and 2b).

Kent Engineering and Foundry Ltd. (K.E.F.) (Plate 6a).

E.C. Large and W. A. R. Dillon Weston and the Editors of *The Journal of Agricultural Science* (Plates 3b and 3c, reproduced from *The Journal of Agricultural Science* (1951), *41*, 4, 338–49).

H. C. Long (Fig. 1 reproduced from his book *The Suppression of Weeds by Fertilizers and Chemicals*, Crosby Lockwood & Son Ltd.).

Pest Control Ltd. (Plate 5b).

F. Randell, Ltd. (Plate 1b).

L. Reeve and Co. Ltd. (the line drawings composing Fig. 2, reproduced from *Illustrations of the British Flora*).

W. Weeks & Son Ltd. (Plate 5a).

The National Seed Testing Station, Cambridge (for providing the "Injurious weed seeds" photographed in Plate 1a).

He also records his sincere thanks for considerable help given by two colleagues at the Hertfordshire Institute of Agriculture, Mr. H. W. Gardner (head of the Agricultural Science Department) and Mr. A. R. Carter, who, besides making helpful criticisms of the final manuscript, have made a number of suggestions most of which have been incorporated.

Finally, he is deeply grateful to his wife, who, apart from acting as typist, critic and proof reader, has made endless cups of tea and has sat patiently and silently during the many evenings spent in writing.

GLOSSARY

A List of Common and Latin Plant Names

Common names of weeds and crop plants, with their Latin equivalents: (*spp.* = species.)

Annual Nettle . .	*Urtica urens.*
Bents . . .	*Agrostis spp.*
Bindweeds . .	*Convolvulus arvensis* and *Polygonum convolvulus.*
Birdsfoot Trefoil . .	*Lotus corniculatus.*
Black Bindweed . .	*Polygonum convolvulus.*
Black Bryony . .	*Tamus communis.*
Black Grass . .	*Alopecurus agrestis*
Black Medick . .	*Medicago lupulina.*
Black Mustard . .	*Brassica nigra.*
Black Nightshade . .	*Solanum nigrum.*
Box	*Buxus sempervirens.*
Bracken . . .	*Pteridium aquilinum.*
Brambles . . .	*Rubus spp.*
Broad-leaved Dock .	*Rumex obtusifolius.*
Broad-leaved Plantain .	*Plantago major.*
Broom . . .	*Sarothamnus scoparius.*
Broomrapes . .	*Orobanche spp.*
Bulbous Buttercup .	*Ranunculus bulbosus.*
Burnets . . .	*Poterium spp.*
Caraway . . .	*Carum carvi.*
Catsear . . .	*Hypochaeris radicata.*
Celandine . . .	*Ranunculus ficaria.*
Celery-leaved Crowfoot .	*Ranunculus sceleratus.*
Chamomiles . .	*Anthemis* and *Matricaria spp.*
Charlock . . .	*Sinapis arvensis.*
Chickweed . . .	*Stellaria media.*
Cinquefoil . . .	*Potentilla reptans.*
Cleavers . . .	*Galium aparine.*

Cocksfoot	. . .	*Dactylis glomerata.*
Common Hemlock	. .	*Conium maculatum.*
Common Henbane	.	*Hyoscyamus niger.*
Common Rush	. .	*Juncus effusus.*
Corn Buttercup	. .	*Ranunculus arvensis.*
Corn Cockle	. .	*Agrostemma githago.*
Cornflower	. . .	*Centaurea cyanus.*
Corn Gromwell	. .	*Lithospermum arvense.*
Corn Marigold	. .	*Chrysanthemum segetum.*
Couch	. . .	*Agropyron repens.*
Cow Parsley	. .	*Anthriscus sylvestris.*
Cranesbills	. . .	*Geranium spp.*
Creeping Buttercup	.	*Ranunculus repens.*
Creeping Soft Grass	.	*Holcus mollis.*
Creeping Thistle	. .	*Cirsium arvense.*
Crowfoots	. . .	*Ranunculus spp.*
Curled Dock	. .	*Rumex crispus.*
Daisy	. . .	*Bellis perennis.*
Dandelion	. . .	*Taraxacum officinale.*
Darnel	. . .	*Lolium tenulentum.*
Deadly Nightshade	.	*Atropa belladonna.*
Dead Nettles	. .	*Lamium spp.*
Docks	. . .	*Rumex spp.*
Dodders	. . .	*Cuscuta spp.*
Earthnut	. . .	*Conopodium majus.*
Elder	. . .	*Sambucus nigra.*
Fat Hen	. . .	*Chenopodium album.*
Fescues	. . .	*Festuca spp.*
Field Mint	. . .	*Mentha arvensis.*
Field Mouse-ear Chickweed	.	*Cerastium arvense.*
Fool's Parsley	. .	*Aethusa cynapium.*
Foxglove	. . .	*Digitalis purpurea.*
Fumitory	. . .	*Fumaria officinalis.*
Greater Celandine	. .	*Chelidonium majus.*
Ground Elder	. .	*Aegopodium podagraria.*
Groundsel	. . .	*Senecio vulgaris.*
Hawkbits	. . .	*Leontodon spp.*
Hawksbeards	. .	*Crepis spp.*
Hawthorns	. . .	*Crataegus spp.*

Hemp Nettles	. .	*Galeopsis spp.*
Hoary Pepperwort	.	*Cardaria draba.*
Horsetails	. .	*Equisetum spp.*
Knapweed	. .	*Centaurea nigra.*
Knawel	. .	*Scleranthus annuus.*
Knotgrass	. .	*Polygonum aviculare.*
Laburnum	. .	*Laburnum anagyroides.*
Lesser Bindweed	.	*Convolvulus arvensis.*
Maple	. .	*Acer campestre.*
Mayweeds	. .	*Anthemis* and *Matricaria spp.*
Meadow Grasses	.	*Poa spp.*
Meadow Saffron	.	*Colchicum autumnale.*
Mouse-ear Chickweed	.	*Cerastium vulgatum.*
Night Shades	.	*Solanum spp.* and *Atropa belladonna.*
Onion Couch	.	*Arrhenatherum tuberosum.*
Ox-eye Daisy	.	*Chrysanthemum leucanthemum.*
Parsley Piert	.	*Aphanes arvensis.*
Pennycress	. .	*Thlaspi arvense.*
Perennial Ryegrass		*Lolium perenne.*
Persicaria	. .	*Polygonum persicaria.*
Poppy	. .	*Papaver rhoeas.*
Privet	. .	*Ligustrum vulgare.*
Ragwort	. .	*Senecio jacobea.*
Ribwort	. .	*Plantago lanceolata.*
Rough Chervil	.	*Chaerophyllum temulum.*
Runch	. .	*Raphanus raphinistrum.*
Rushes	. .	*Juncus spp.*
Sandworts	. .	*Arenaria spp.*
Scabious	. .	*Scabiosa arvensis*
Scarlet Pimpernel	.	*Anagallis arvensis.*
Scentless Mayweed	.	*Matricaria maritima.*
Sedges	. .	*Carex spp.*
Selfheal	. .	*Prunella vulgaris.*
Sheep's Fescue	.	*Festuca ovina.*
Sheep's Sorrel	.	*Rumex acetosella.*
Shepherd's Needle	.	*Scandix pecten-veneris.*
Shepherd's Purse	.	*Capsella bursa-pastoris.*
Soft Brome	.	*Bromus mollis.*

Sorrels	. . .	*Rumex spp.*
Sowthistle	. . .	*Sonchus oleraceus.*
Spear Thistle	. .	*Cirsium vulgare.*
Speedwells	. .	*Veronica spp.*
Spurrey	. .	*Spergula arvensis.*
Stinging Nettle	. .	*Urtica dioica.*
Tall Buttercup	. .	*Ranunculus acris.*
Tansy	. .	*Tanacetum vulgare.*
Thrift	. .	*Armeria maritima.*
Timothy	. .	*Phleum pratense.*
Treacle Mustard	. .	*Erysimum cheiranthoides.*
Vetch	. .	*Vicia sativa.*
Water Dropwort	. .	*Oenanthe fistulosa.*
Water Hemlock	. .	*Circuta virosa.*
Water Parsnip	. .	*Sium latifolium.*
White Mustard	. .	*Sinapis alba.*
Wild Carrot	. .	*Daucus carota.*
Wild Chervil	. .	*Anthriscus cerefolium.*
Wild Oat	. .	*Avena fatua* and *A. ludoviciana.*
Wild Onion	. .	*Allium vineale.*
Wild Roses	. .	*Rosa spp.*
Wild White Clover	. .	*Trifolium repens var. sylvestre.*
Yarrow	. .	*Achillea millefolium.*
Yellow Rattle	. .	*Rhinanthus minor.*
Yellow Suckling Clover	.	*Trifolium dubium.*
Yew	. .	*Taxus baccata.*
Yorkshire Fog	. .	*Holcus lanatus.*

ALTERNATIVE COMMON NAMES OF SOME BRITISH WEEDS

Annual Nettle . .	Small Nettle.
Avéns . . .	Herb-Bennett.
Black Bindweed .	Bearbind.
Blackgrass .	Slender Foxtail.
Bladder Campion .	Billy Buttons, White-bottle.
Bracken . . .	Brake.
Charlock .	Wild Mustard, Kilk.
Cleavers . . .	Sweethearts, Goosegrass, Hariff.
Corn Buttercup .	Beggar's Lice.
Cornflower .	Bluebottle.
Couch . . .	Twitch, Quitch, Scutch, Wicks, Quack Grass.
Earthnut . .	Pignut.
Fat Hen . . .	Lamb's Quarters, Dungweed, Goosefoot.
Field Bindweed .	Lesser Bindweed.
Ground Elder .	Goutweed, Bishop's Weed.
Heartsease .	Wild Pansy.
Hemp Nettle .	Day Nettle.
Hoary Pepperwort .	Hoary Cress, Thanet Weed, White Weed, Devil's Cabbage.
Hogweed . .	Cow Parsnip
Horsetail .	Marestail, Snake Pipe.
Jack-by-the-hedge .	Garlic Mustard.
Knapweed .	Hardheads.
Knotgrass .	Knotweed, Iron Weed, Wire Weed.
Nightshade .	Bittersweet
Ox-eye Daisy .	Dog Daisy.
Parsley Piert .	Lady's Mantle.
Persicaria .	Redshank, Willow Weed.
Potentilla .	Cinquefoil.

Ribwort .	.	.	Narrow-leaved Plantain, Ribgrass.
Runch .	.	.	Wild Radish, White Charlock.
Speedwell	.	.	Birdseye.
Tall Buttercup		.	Crowfoot.
Wild Onion	.	.	Crow Garlic.
Willow Herb	.	.	Blitzweed.
Yarrow .	.	.	Milfoil.

THE MEANINGS OF SOME LATIN WORDS USED IN NAMES OF PLANTS

NOTE: Although the endings of the Latin words given below may vary, the meaning is unaltered. The possible variations in ending are as follows:

Names ending in "-us" may also end in "-a" or "-um".
     ,,   ,,   ,, "-is" ,, ,, ,, ,, "-e".
     ,,   ,,   ,, "-er" ,, ,, ,, ,, "-ra" or "-rum".

Thus in different plant names the word niger may also be rendered as nigra or nigrum, but in every case it means "black".

Acris	. . .	"sharp" or "pungent".
Agrostis	. . .	"of the field".
Albus	. . .	"white".
Arvensis	. . .	"of cultivated fields".
Asper	. . .	"rough".
Bulbosus	. . .	"bulbous".
Campestris	. . .	"of the plain".
Crispus	. . .	"curled".
Elatior	. . .	"taller".
Glomeratus	. . .	"clustered".
Lanatus	. . .	"woolly".
Mollis	. . .	"soft".
Niger	. . .	"black".
Obtusifolius	. . .	"with broad leaves".
Officinalis	. . .	"medicinal".
Ovinus	. . .	"of sheep".
Pratensis	. . .	"of the meadow".
Repens	. . .	"creeping".
Ruber	. . .	"red".
Segetum	. . .	"of the cornfield".
Urens	. . .	"burning" or "stinging".
Vulgaris	. . .	"common".

APPENDIX I

OFFICIAL SEED TESTING STATIONS IN THE BRITISH ISLES

ENGLAND AND WALES
>The Official Seed Testing Station,
>>Huntingdon Road,
>>>Cambridge

SCOTLAND
>>Seed Testing, Plant Registration and Plant Pathology Station,
>>East Craigs,
>>>Corstorphine,
>>>>Edinburgh 12

N. IRELAND
>>Seed Testing Station,
>>Queen's University,
>>>Elmwood Avenue,
>>>>Belfast

APPENDIX II

THE CHEMICAL NAMES AND FORMULAE OF THE WEEDKILLERS

In this appendix the weedkillers mentioned in the book are listed, in alphabetical order, under their common names or abbreviations. They are accompanied by their true chemical names and formulae as follows:

(*a*) The true chemical name if different from the common name.

(*b*) The empirical formula (organic substances) or usual formula (inorganic substances).

(*c*) The structural formula (for organic substances only).

(*d*) The chemical name, if different from (*a*), from which the popular abbreviation (if any) is taken.

(1) *B.O.V.*
   (*a*) Sulphuric acid (77%).
   (*b*) H_2SO_4.
   (*d*) Brown Oil of Vitriol.

(2) *Calcium cyanamide.*
   (*b*) $CaCN_2$.
   (*c*) NC.NCa.

(3) *C.M.U.*
   (*a*) 3-(*p*-chlorophenyl)-1 : 1-dimethyl urea.
   (*b*) $C_9H_{11}ClN_2O$.
   (*c*)

NH.CO.N(CH₃)₂.

Cl

(4) *Copper chloride*.
    (*a*) Cupric chloride.
    (*b*) $CuCl_2,2H_2O$.

(5) 2,4-*D. or D.C.P.A.*
    (*a*) 2,4-dichlorophenoxyacetic acid.
    (*b*) $C_8H_6Cl_2O_3$.
    (*c*)

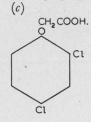

Sodium salt.

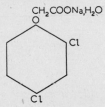

*Iso*propyl ester.

(6) *D.N.B.P.* or dinoseb.
    (*a*) 2-sec,-butyl-4:6-dinitrophenol.
    (*b*) $C_{10}H_{12}N_2O_5$.
    (*c*)

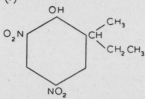

    (*d*) Dinitro-secondary-butyl-phenol.

(7) *D.N.O.C.* or *D.N.C.*
    (*a*) 2-methyl-4:6-dinitrophenol.
    (*b*) $C_7H_6N_2O_5$.
    (*c*)

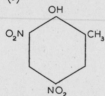

    (*d*) Dinitro-ortho-cresol.

(8) *M.C.P.A.*
    (*a*) 2-methyl-4-chlorophenoxyacetic acid.
    (*b*) $C_9H_9ClO_3$.

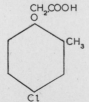

(9) *Sodium chlorate.*
    (b) NaClO$_3$.

(10) *Sulphate of ammonia.*
    (a) Ammonium sulphate.
    (b) (NH$_4$)$_2$SO$_4$.

(11) *Sulphate of iron (calcined).*
    (a) Anhydrous ferrous sulphate.
    (b) FeSO$_4$.

(12) 2,4,5-*T.*
    (a) 2,4,5-trichlorophenoxyacetic acid.
    (b) C$_8$H$_5$Cl$_3$O$_3$.
    (c)

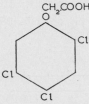

The structural formulae of the sodium salt and *iso*propyl ester are formed as in 2,4-D.

(13) *T.C.A.*
    (a) Trichloroacetic acid.
    (b) C$_2$Cl$_3$HO$_2$.
    (c)

Further details regarding the chemical nature of the weed-killers, their analysis and preparation can be found in *Guide to the Chemicals Used in Crop Protection*, by H. Martin and J. R. W. Miles, published by the Canadian Department of Agriculture.

INDEX

NOTES

Main references are given in heavy type. References to illustrations are given in italics.
In all references to plants the common name used is as given in the Glossary.

A

Acid equivalent, **67** *et seq.*
Acidity:
  choice of fertilizers, 41
  correction of, 37, 38, 39
  of lawns, **42**
Acid-resisting materials, **124**, 129
Acids, 58, **67** *et seq.* (*see also* B.O.V., Sulphuric acid)
  burning effect, 57
  nature of D.N.O.C., 86
Actinomycosis, 23
Activators, **87**
Adaptability of spraying machines, 129
Aeration, 47
Agitators, 87, **127**, 129
Agriculture (Poisonous Substances) Regulations, **89**, 90
"Agropyron", **133**
Alfalfa (*see* Lucerne)
Alsike clover, 33, 34 (*see also* Clovers)
Ammonium sulphate (*see* Sulphate of ammonia)
Anguillulina dipsaci (*see* Tulip Root)
Animals, 77 (*see also* Cattle, Cows, Pigs, Sheep)
  carriers of seeds, 27, **28**
Annual Meadow Grass, 116
Annual Nettle, 37, 81, 85, 86, 88, 91, 93, 94, 99, 117
Annual Sowthistle, 118 (*see also* Sowthistle)
Annual weeds, 62
  control with Sodium chlorate, 80
Aphelenchoides ritzema-bosi (*see* Chrysanthemum Eelworm)
Aromatic content, **92**
Arsenic, 58
Arvensis, 70
Asparagus, 94, **113**, 154
Atlacide, **76**
Autumn cleaning, **54** *et seq.*, 140

B

Bare Fallow, **51** *et seq.*, 55, 56, 136, 143
  against Couch, 132
Barley, 20, 25, 33, 60, 79, 100, 142 (*see also* Cereals)
  occurrence of bowed ears, 101
Basic slag, 41
Bastard fallow, 51, **53**
  against Couch, 132
Beans, 33, 143
  use of weedkillers, **107**
Bedstraw, 116
Bees, **120**
Beet, 33, 79 (*see also* Mangolds, Root crops, Sugar beet)
Bents, 24, 38, 81, 132
Bindweeds, 81
Birds, 77
  carriers of seeds, 27, **28**
Black Bindweed, 84, 86, 88, 91, 116
Black Bryony, 22
Blackgrass, 55
  control of, 37
Blackman, G. E., 92, 137, 152
Black Medick, 116
Black Mustard, 22
Black Nightshade, 24, 27, 91
Bladder Campion, 116
Blasting, 101
Bonnet, 152
Boom, 125, **126**, 130, 131
Boot stage, 101
Bordeaux mixture, 83, 129
B.O.V., **85** *et seq.*, 100, 128, 129, 152
  against Bracken, 147
  against Dodder, 135
  machines for applying, 123, **124**
  precautions, 131
  use for pre-emergence application, 102
  use in bulbs, **113**
  use in cereals, **101**
  use in onions and leeks, **111**

H

I

J